Recognition : A STUDY IN THE PHILOSOPHY OF ARTIFICIAL INTELLIGENCE

Recognition: A STUDY

IN THE PHILOSOPHY OF

ARTIFICIAL INTELLIGENCE

by Kenneth M. Sayre

 UNIVERSITY OF NOTRE DAME PRESS

1965

28511

TO THREE BOYS AND THEIR MOTHER

PREFACE

Parts Two and Three of this book contain a philosophic analysis of the concepts of recognition and of allied perceptual acts. They may be read independently of the other parts. Readers primarily oriented towards computer applications, on the other hand, may wish to pass directly from Part One to Part Four. To readers of the first sort, Parts Two and Three might appear as the meat in the sandwich; to the other they might appear merely as stuffing in the fowl.

I wish in no way to discourage readers of either sort. Yet it may be confessed that the book is written for persons who will find something natural in the transition from Part One to Part Two, and who are prepared to find in Part Four a concrete fulfillment of the conceptual analysis in the parts preceding. These are likely to be persons whose interest lies somewhere along the boundaries between the field of artificial intelligence and what has at various times been called "analytic psychology," "philosophical psychology," or simply "philosophy of mind." I hope that the reader of this latter sort will be gratified by the way in which the tools of the analyst can be turned into instruments of discovery for the simulation specialist, and by the way conversely in which the prospect of computer simulation provides a criterion of clarity and relevance for the conceptual analysis of mental acts.

Acknowledgment is gratefully rendered to the National Science Foundation for support of the study from which this book resulted, and to the University of Notre Dame for time, facilities and early encouragement. I wish in particular to thank the Reverend Chester A. Soleta, C.S.C., the Reverend Herman R. Reith, C.S.C., Dr. George N. Shuster and Dr. Joseph Bobik, all of the University of Notre Dame, each of whom gave assistance which was essential at the outset of the study. The manuscript was read by Professors Vere Chappell of the University of Chicago, Milton Fisk of Yale University and Frederick Crosson of the University of Notre Dame. Much of what is good in the book is due to their incisive criticism and helpful advice, for which I am especially grateful.

I wish also to thank Professors R. B. Braithwaite, M. Eden, F. H. George, L. Uhr, and Dr. J. C. R. Licklider, as well as the editors of *Philosophy* and the editorial board of the Institute of Electronic and Electrical Engineers, for permission to quote passages on pp. 166–167, p. 41, p. 32, p. 39, and pp. 23–24 below.

CONTENTS

[ix

IV. THE RECOGNITION
OF LETTER-INSCRIPTIONS   199

INTRODUCTION

1. Although 'artificial intelligence' refers more to a set of goals than to an accomplished fact, there has been enough progress towards these goals recently to incite interest within practically every experimental science of human behavior. 'Artificial intelligence' has become a standard phrase as well among philosophers, analytical psychologists, neurophysiologists and electrical engineers.

The term 'artificial' in this use serves as the adjectival form of 'artifact'. The artifacts here in point are mechanical systems, usually based upon digital computers. Each component of such a system is an object of human contrivance. Yet when the components are arranged in certain ways, these systems can exhibit behavior which to some extent resembles procedures of the human intellect. When this happens, we say that the system *simulates* an aspect of intelligent human behavior.

Let us then understand the expression 'artificial intelligence' to refer to the desired results of attempts to simulate various aspects of intelligent human behavior in mechanical systems based upon digital computers. Several attempts of this sort are now in progress, and the difficulties encountered in some of these attempts set the problem for this essay.

Our particular concern is with human pattern-recognition, and with certain conceptual obscurities which are blocking current attempts to simulate it. These obscurities are in part methodological. Given the present "state of the art" (which probably no one would consider to reflect a high level of achievement in simulation studies), we have no clear notion of what should be done to gain significant improvement in the performance of our simulation mechanisms. The reason for this is that we do not know exactly what is going wrong; and the reason for this in turn is that we lack appropriate criteria for judging the adequacy of our present results. Behind these methodological obscurities, however, is an unclarity about the nature of the human behavior we are trying to simulate. We simply do not understand what recognition is. And if we do not understand the behavior we are trying to simulate, we cannot reasonably hold high hopes of being successful in our attempts to simulate it.

At the heart of these conceptual difficulties is a fundamental confusion between recognition and classification. That recognition has been conceived by researchers in the area to be a form of classification is evident to anyone familiar with the literature of mechanical pattern-recognition. Yet the distinction between recognition and classification is so unmistakable that once it has been made articulate it will appear strange that we should ever have fallen prey to the confusion.

Although simulation studies with digital computers are still in their infancy, the confusion between classification and recognition has already begun to show practical consequences. Part of our task is to trace out some of the more undesirable of these consequences. We will then show how the difficulties posed by these consequences can be avoided when we approach the simulation problem under the guidance of a more adequate conception of what it is to recognize a pattern.

The method of this essay is conceptual analysis. This is reflected within the structure of the book. Part One develops the concept of simulation, summarizes results to date in the simulation of human pattern-recognition, and locates the basic confusion between classification and recognition which sets the task for the chapters which follow. Part Two establishes the conceptual distinction between processes and attainments, and shows the fundamental importance of this distinction for understanding the relationship between classification and recognition. In Part Three the concept of recognition is examined in detail with regard to the differences among recognition and the closely related mental acts of sensation and perception. With this conceptual background we are able finally in Part Four to develop a new model for mechanical pattern-recognition in terms of Information Theory. This model, in which recognition is equated with the reception of information, clarifies several things about the problem of simulating human recognition which remain obscure as long as recognition is conceived as a form of classification. In the final chapter the results of the analysis, focused through the Information-Theoretic model, are translated into specifications for a new approach to mechanical pattern-recognition.

Although the practical results of this essay thus fall within the area of simulation studies, the theoretical results bear upon important problems currently under discussion in analytic psychology and in the philosophy of mind. By removing the fog of the confusion between classification and recognition, not only are we able to see why present pattern-recognition mechanisms are unsatisfactory, but also we are able to remove some basic misunderstandings about the nature of mental acts which are evident in contemporary philosophic and psychological literature. The particular conceptual problems which have beset simulation specialists recently in fact bear an instructive resemblance to problems with which, in a more general form, philosophers have been wrestling for centuries. Now that these problems can be seen to have an immediate practical bearing, the philosopher has been provided a feedback, previously unavailable, which serves to keep his analysis on a clear and pertinent track.

Thus insofar as this essay is successful, it contains results of interest both to philosophers and to those engineers and scientists concerned with the simulation of human behavior on computers. It should be of interest also to those psychologists and sociologists who have been puzzled about the role of models in our study of human behavior. Beyond these areas of immediate interest, however, the essay establishes the feasibility of a fruitful interchange of methodology and results between two previously disparate approaches to mental phenomena—philosophy and computer simulation. It thereby displays the outlines of a new field of constructive inquiry which might someday warrant a special title. Perhaps "The Philosophy of Artificial Intelligence" would be appropriate.

2. The topic of mechanical pattern-recognition does not engage public fancy as readily as do stories of electronic computers which play chess, compose music or prove mathematical theorems. Perhaps this is because the application of computers to pattern-recognition, unlike those other applications, does not seem at first to threaten our conception of the uniqueness of the human mind. This comports with the approach of this essay, which does not leave room for speculation about what differences there may be between minds and machines. Questions

about the relationship between minds and machines are interesting and important, but they are not relevant to the present study.

At the same time, the eventual achievement of successful pattern-recognition mechanisms is a matter of first-rank importance. This is so for several reasons, some of which can be briefly noted. There are, of course, various practical applications for such mechanisms. A reliable recognizer of imperfectly formed visual patterns could be developed into a mechanical reader for the blind, or into an automatic mail sorter with a flexibility comparable to that of its present human counterpart. An audible pattern recognizer when coupled with an automatic encoder would provide a more efficient means of communicating with computers than any technique now available, or when combined with a typing device could produce an impeccably typed letter within seconds after the end of dictation. These and other possible practical applications are reviewed in Chapter Two below. Although the desirability of these practical applications constitutes part of the justification for this study, they are not among the topics due for detailed discussion.

Another dimension of importance is reflected in the fact that the problems of automatic pattern-recognition are central within the more spectacular areas of artificial intelligence mentioned above. The difference between a master and a novice at chess, for example, lies in the ability of the master to recognize a good or a bad position on the board for what it is, whether he encounters it in play or in the anticipation of future moves. To remark that this is the case is not in itself to advance the art of mechanical chess. But it is not without interest to conjecture that the essential difference between mechanical chess-players and mechanical letter-readers has more to do with different types of patterns to be recognized than with different techniques of data processing.

Similar remarks apply to the relationship between pattern-recognition and the mechanical composition of music. According to a recent account of the nature of musical composition, "the formation of a piece of music is an ordering process in which specified musical elements are selected and arranged from an infinite variety of possibilities, i.e., from chaos."[1] It is harmonious with this definition to think of musical composition as consisting of two related but distinct activities. The first is the selection of a few specific musical elements and combinations of elements out of an unlimited number of possible combinations. The second is an assessment of the aesthetic value of each of these specific combinations, relative to the intentions of the composer and to other combinations which he has selected or is contemplating. The first task probably is never undertaken in isolation from the second; but insofar as it could be performed independently, the first task would have little to do with pattern-recognition. The second task, however, is essentially a matter of distinguishing combinations of notes, pauses and inflections which have a high degree of aesthetic value from those which do not. This in turn is a matter of recognizing musical sequences which exhibit a certain type of pattern.

It is worth remarking how similar the task of the composer appears, when viewed in this fashion, to the task of the creative mathematician. Every proof in mathematics consists in an obvious sense of a sequence of symbols, the ordering of which is essential to the proof. It is a routine matter for anyone familiar with the notation of a formal

---

[1] From *Experimental Music*, by Lejaren Hiller and Leonard Isaacson (New York, McGraw-Hill Book Company, Inc., 1959), p. 16. Reprinted in part in *The Modeling of Mind*, eds. Kenneth Sayre and Frederick Crosson (Notre Dame, University of Notre Dame Press, 1963).

system to construct symbol sequences which can be given an interpretation within the system. The skill of the mathematician comes into evidence only when he attempts to discover or to impose within a sequence of symbols those particular patterns which count towards the accomplishment of a formal proof. Whether a sequence of symbols constitutes a proof within a given formal system depends upon the intelligible patterns constituted by the symbols within the sequence. The differences within mathematics among valid proofs, invalid proofs and nonsense are in this way analogous to the differences within music among good composition, bad composition and chaos.

The problem of building a mechanical composer of music may be conceived in this manner as a particular aspect of the more general problem of finding a way to make a machine capable of recognizing patterns of sound which have certain aesthetic values for the human listener. At a comparable level of generality, the basic problem of mechanical mathematics is to build a machine capable of distinguishing among patterns of symbols which are interpretable in certain ways by the skilled mathematician. In view of this, another by-product which might be expected from an effective pattern-recognition device is a set of techniques which could be applied in improved music-composition and theorem-proving systems.

Of more intrinsic importance than any of these applications is the increase in our understanding of human recognitive behavior which would accompany the development of more effective mechanical recognition systems. Our understanding of a type of human behavior and our ability to simulate it go hand in hand. What is not understood, on the one hand, can be no more than crudely simulated. When we become capable of simulating the behavior of a particular physical or biological system, on the other hand, this often leads to a better understanding of that behavior itself. The flight of birds, for example, could be imitated only after we had begun to understand aerodynamics. Yet our knowledge of flight has increased with the study of models which merely simulate the conditions of actual flight.

The possibility of using mechanical simulation as a research tool in the study of mental behavior has begun to be discussed only very recently, and the growth of conceptual clarity which might be gained by this technique has scarcely been discussed at all.[2] No great conceptual sophistication is required to build a machine that works along the same principles as the human arm. The principles of leverage and constriction involved in this action are understood, can be articulated, and present no immediate conceptual difficulties. But we do not understand the human behavior associated with the recognition of patterns with comparable clarity and thoroughness. One way of improving our conceptual grasp of this behavior, available now for the first time in the recorded history of science, is through the attempt to articulate our conceptions in the medium of a mechanical simulation system and to re-examine our conceptions critically in light of the results.

An example of this process is provided by the experiments in the mechanical composition of music cited above. One of the first steps in this procedure is to arrive at a plausible analysis of the principles of composition which appear to be involved in the work of accomplished human composers. Attempts to analyze principles of this sort, it is true, have not been limited to musicology within the past decade, or even within this century. But

---

2 In this regard, however, see D. M. MacKay's "Towards an Information-Flow Model of Human Behaviour," *The British Journal of Psychology*, XLVII (1956), 31.

in the past, such attempts could be evaluated primarily in theory only, and hence remained speculative. With the development of computer systems to the point where it became feasible to simulate the function of the composer, the musicologist has been provided with a "laboratory" to test his theories. If persistent attempts to compose music mechanically on the basis of a given set of principles fail to produce good music, there is reason to believe that more is involved in composition than is articulated in these principles alone. When this happens, it would be in order for the musicologist to isolate specific respects in which his results were disappointing and to attempt to determine whether any part of his analysis of the principles of composition might be altered to give improved results in these respects. Apart from the better music which could result from this procedure, the musicologist might well expect to gain an increased understanding of the function of composition itself, and of what it is that distinguishes the human composer of genius from less gifted persons.

A similar application of simulation techniques can lead to an increased understanding of human pattern-recognition. Pattern-recognition mechanisms currently at hand illustrate the consequences of thinking about recognition in a particular way. This concept of recognition has not been clearly articulated by any of the specialists working under its influence, but it can be reconstructed from the results of their work and from what they say about it. An analysis of this particular conception might be expected to exhibit conceptual shortcomings which can be correlated with specific difficulties encountered in attempts, based upon it, to construct workable recognition mechanisms. A constructive result of such an analysis would be to suggest ways of overcoming some of these difficulties on the basis of a more clearly articulated and more defensible conception of the behavior to be simulated.

Thus we turn again to the aim of the present study. As suggested above, there is an unmistakable tendency on the part of specialists concerned with mechanical pattern-recognition to conceive the recognition of an object as being identical with the classification of that object. It can be shown conclusively, however, that recognition and classification are very different activities indeed, and that when someone conceives recognition in such a fashion as to blur this distinction he will overlook certain aspects of recognitive behavior which are essential for its satisfactory simulation. This is only one of the conceptual aberrations plaguing current research in mechanical pattern-recognition, but this alone probably accounts for more lost motion and wasted time than the administrators of simulation research projects would care to imagine.

In order to gain conceptual clarity about what is required of an adequate pattern-recognition system, and to avoid costly practical mistakes which follow unclear thinking about this type of behavior, we have no better course than to analyze the concept of recognition associated with typical recognitive behavior of human beings. We shall concentrate in particular upon the behavior associated with the recognition of letter-inscriptions. The results of this analysis, insofar as it is successful, will include (1) a clearer conception of the structure of the behavior to be simulated in mechanical recognition devices, (2) a better understanding of the difficulties encountered in current attempts to simulate this behavior, and (3) suggestions of how the simulation task might be conceived in order to avoid problems which from another point of view might seem unavoidable.

Recognition : A STUDY IN THE PHILOSOPHY OF ARTIFICIAL INTELLIGENCE

PART I

MODELS

AND

CONCEPTS

CHAPTER ONE

THE NEW ART
OF SIMULATION

1. There is a clear sense in which a college library might be modeled after the Parthenon, and a relatively clear sense in which the flight of a bird is modeled by an airplane. But the sense in which human mental behavior can be modeled by a machine may seem initially to be rather puzzling. Since our concern in the pages which follow is with the mechanical modeling of human pattern-recognition, it is best that we become clear at the outset about how modeling of this sort might be accomplished.

Only a few decades ago the term 'model' had no established technical use among scientists. Yet today it is used confidently and with facility not only by physicists and mathematicians, but also by psychologists, biologists, sociologists, economists and political theorists. Since most researchers in the area of artificial intelligence at this stage have migrated from these more traditional disciplines, the notion of a computer-based model of mental behavior has a familiarity which may be too easily mistaken for clarity. There are, in fact, several ways in which human behavior might be modeled, and more than one way in which human behavior can be modeled mechanically. But there seems to be only one way in which human *mental* behavior can be modeled on a *computer*, and this involves modeling of a type quite different from anything found within the traditional techniques of experimental science.

In the attempt to make this clear we will distinguish three different ways (among others) in which an object or activity might be modeled. These will be designated in turn (a) 'replication', (b) 'formalization' and (c) 'simulation'. After discussing in general terms the differences among these ways, we will examine simulation in more detail.[1]

(a) 'Replication' is a loose-jointed term intended for the present to cover various duplications, reproductions, facsimiles and dummies. The college library fashioned after the Parthenon is an example, as would be most statues, all reproductions of statues, some paintings, and various playthings such as dolls, toy cars and plastic guns. The purpose of objects like these generally is one of pleasure, recreation or ceremony. Different from these in function, but replications nonetheless, are the models of the motor coach designer, the airfoils of the aerodynamical engineer, and the various earth-bound panels and chambers used in designing space enclosures for astronauts. A replication of yet another sort designed for research is the war exercise with which military planners experiment in peace time with new battle tactics and weapons. The general purpose of research techniques based on models like these is to provide for the testing of behavior and design characteristics of objects and processes which either are not available for direct study, or the variables of which do not admit convenient control and measurement.

---

[1] The discussion here is patterned after Chapter One of *The Modeling of Mind*, eds. Kenneth Sayre and Frederick Crosson (Notre Dame, University of Notre Dame Press, 1963), pp. 3–18. The former material, however, has been revised, and some problems previously lurking in the background have been brought closer to the light.

The common feature in these examples is that in each some prominent physical characteristic of the original object or process is reproduced in the replication. Both war exercises and actual combat, for example, employ soldiers and battle equipment. And the research space capsule is adequate for its purpose only insofar as its controls look, feel and act like their counterparts in an actual space vehicle. A mere photograph of a space capsule, however, is not a replication; for whereas a space capsule is a three-dimensional object constructed out of metal and ceramics, a photograph is two-dimensional and in the relevant sense not constructed out of anything. A statue of Caesar is a replication, insofar as it reproduces some features of the man. But a statue of Pegasus is not a replication because there are no original physical features to be reproduced. A drawing of a statue, even by the same artist, is never a replication, for no physical features of the original are present as such in the drawing—at best some are represented. But a photograph of an artist's sketch is a replication, for here the lines originally traced by the artist's pen are reproduced in lines traced by chemical action.

Although there are limitations of this sort upon the degree of dissimilarity between a replication and its original, there seems to be no limitation in regard to similarity. If there were a reproduction of the Parthenon which is like the original (at a given stage of dissolution) in every respect, save in being constructed out of different pieces of stone, it would still be a replication. And a plaster-of-Paris copy of a statue would count as a replication without regard to the high precision with which the copy matches the original.

Most of our examples thus far are reproductions of static features of objects. The term 'replication' is intended to be broad enough also to cover not only reproductions of processes, as in the war exercise, but certain behavioral characteristics of animals and machines as well. In considering replications of behavior it seems natural to think first of ways in which the actions of mechanical systems might be reproduced. Exhibits in automotive fairs and salesrooms often feature "cutaway" models of gasoline engines which are powered by hidden electric motors. The purpose of these models is to replicate the action of the valves, drive rods and shafts of an engine operating in an automobile. We would not say, on the other hand, that the operation of an actual engine produced on an assembly line replicates the operation of the prototype engine constructed by the designers. Herein lies a difference between replicating the static features of an object and replicating the operating features of a behavioral system. While there seems to be no limit in degree of similarity between the static model and its original, there do appear to be limits of this sort between the operation of one system and the operation of another system which might be said to replicate it. Given two statues which appear to be identical in shape, or nearly so, it seems natural to wonder which is the original and which is the copy. But given two engines which seem identical or nearly identical in function, it does not seem natural to question which is the copy of the other.

With the expression "identical in function," however, we have begun to say things relevant to modeling of a different sort which has yet to be clarified. While our remarks under the present heading are not exhaustive, they are adequate at least for a comparison of replications and formal models. A typical feature of the formal model is that it does not reproduce any of the physical characteristics of the original system.

(b) In a formal model, both the components of the system modeled and the interconnections among these components are represented by symbols which can be manipulated according to the provisions of a well-defined formal discipline, typically a branch of logic or mathematics. Although there is a sense in which a mathematical description of an egg or a doughnut is a model, consideration here will be limited to those formal models which represent systems of operations or modes of behavior, in distinction from "merely static" characteristics of objects.

Consider how the behavior of a system of interconnected switches, each capable of exactly two positions, can be studied by a model provided by a two-valued logic with the operations of conjunction and negation. The switches may be represented within the model by logical variables, and the interaction between any two switches or sets of switches can be represented by an appropriate grouping of logical operators. Since logical operators and variables can be "controlled" more readily than interactions among systems of actual switching devices, it is advantageous for some purposes to study those interactions within the formal structure provided by the logical model. A typical use of a formal model, indeed, is to study interactions among components or behavioral aspects of systems which themselves cannot be conveniently controlled within the provisions of natural or civil law.

There are at least two respects, however, in which a logical model of a switching circuit is not typical of formal models generally. First, in this model each working component of the circuit can be identified and represented individually by a distinct variable. Second, to every change in the circuit from one distinct set of switch positions to another there corresponds within the model a change from one distinct set of values of logical variables to another. In this intuitive sense, the behavior of the model seems to be structurally isomorphic to the behavior of the circuit itself. An example of a formal model which has neither of these characteristics is provided by an equation known, within a discipline currently called "Operations Research," as "Lanchester's N-square Law." This equation illustrates both the strength and the weakness of the formal model.

According to Lanchester's N-square Law, the "fighting strength" of a combat force "may be broadly defined as proportional to the square of its numerical strength multiplied by the fighting value of its individual units."[2] If the individual units of two armies are of equal effectiveness, their relative strength is measured by the proportion of the squares of the numbers of fighting units in actual combat. Thus, for example, by sundering the enemy's forces and concentrating total fire power upon first one and then the other segment, an army can meet with equal fighting strength an enemy greater in numbers by as much as the square root of two.[3]

This law applies in the ideal to a situation in which each combat unit is able to engage each unit of the opposing force, an ideal more closely approached in combat with long-range weapons than in hand-to-hand combat. The major shortcoming of this law as a means for studying the dynamics of actual military combat, however, is the fact that application of the law to particular circumstances will involve the assumption that all factors other than manpower which influence the tides of battle are constant. As Lanchester himself remarked, "superior morale or better tactics or a hundred and one other extraneous causes may intervene in practice to modify the issue," although this is claimed not to "invalidate the mathematical statement" of the law.[4] Because of its very simplicity, Lanchester's model

---

[2] *Aircraft in Warfare*, quoted in *The World of Mathematics*, ed. James R. Newman (New York, Simon and Schuster, 1956), p. 2145.

[3] Consider that force A and force B number respectively n and $n\sqrt{2}$ units. If A encounters separately one half and then the other half of B's forces, the total fighting strengths of A and B are equal, since

$$n^2 = \left(\frac{n\sqrt{2}}{2}\right)^2 + \left(\frac{n\sqrt{2}}{2}\right)^2.$$

[4] *Aircraft in Warfare* (see fn. 2 above), p. 2146.

of combat by itself is of little use as a research tool for studying the variables of actual combat.

The strength of a model of the type illustrated by this example, on the other hand, lies in the fact that it can be solved by known formal techniques. The behavior of the variables within the model can be studied under a variety of conditions by strictly formal manipulations, without regard for problems of feasibility involved in bringing the actual system represented by the model into corresponding physical circumstances.

As research techniques, indeed, the methods of replication and of formalization complement each other in their relative strengths and weaknesses. Compare a full-scale military exercise, for example, with Lanchester's equation as research implements for studying interactions among armed forces in combat. While the N-square Law, or any other formal model comparable to it in generality, necessarily involves some simplification regarding a number of factors pertinent to the study, it seems that the only limitations upon the realism of a battle exercise are imposed by moral and humane considerations. The strength of the formal model, on the other hand, is in the precision of control which it allows over the interrelations among its variables, while with the battle exercise it is practically impossible to maintain adequate control over even the more accessible of the variables which it may be intended to study.

The feature of formal models which distinguishes them most sharply from replications is the fact that the representation they afford of the original system is entirely symbolic. As we shall see, this feature tends also to be characteristic of simulation models. The essential distinction between formal models and simulations, in turn, is a matter of whether the symbolic functions which constitute the model are capable of analytic solution. We will say that the set of symbolic expressions is analytic, and hence that it provides a formal model of a system to be studied, if all equations within the set which symbolize operations of the system can be solved by known and practicable techniques of formal manipulation. These techniques might be provided by set theory, game theory, theory of equations, theory of probability, Boolean algebra, the theory of propositions, or any other system of formal relationships which provides solution-routines applicable to all equations expressible within the system. A set of expressions which cannot be solved analytically, on the other hand, either in theory or in practice, is the mark of a simulation model.

(c) The distinction between formal modeling and simulation comes into focus when one turns to consider the practical requirements of these two methods of modeling. Useful results should be obtainable from a formal model by paper-and-pencil operations on the part of a competent and patient mathematician. A computer might be employed to relieve the tedium of routine calculations, or to speed the result. But the result in any case is an analytic solution to a set of general equations which might be hoped to illuminate some general aspect of the workings of the system under study. It is essential for the application of a simulation model, on the other hand, to have available the services either of an electronic computer or of a battery of clerks with hand computers and a great deal of time. The equations with which the computing facility works, although not capable of analytic solutions in a general form, must admit solution in terms of specific numerical values of their dependent variables for all admissible combinations of numerical values given to their independent variables. The behavior of the equations in general can be estimated by obtaining particular solutions over a sufficiently wide range of numerical values for its more important variables. A statistical description of a large number of particular solutions under typical conditions might be every bit as useful in the application of the model as a general solution would be if one were available.

A very simple illustration will indicate the flexibility of the simulation method. Suppose a set of two equations gives a unique value for x under each admissible combination of values of w, y and z. Since there are four unknowns, but only two equations, it is not possible to solve the equations in a way which exhibits a direct relationship between x and y alone. Thus, if one's motivation in forming the model is to study the interactions between two aspects of a working system which have been symbolized by these two variables, no strictly formal technique is available for that purpose. But one's purpose might be served adequately if one were able to determine the relationship between x and y under a representative sampling of the values admitted by the other variables. This could be accomplished by allowing w and z to vary through a range of typical values, selected according to the particular purpose of the study, and computing x as a function of y for all combinations of these values of w and z. It might be possible to represent x as a probabilistic function of y, within these particular ranges of values for w and x, or even to approximate an exact relationship between x and y under those conditions which one considers particularly important for the study. One's estimation of which conditions in regard to z and w are important, of course, may change as the study progresses. The researcher's first application of the model may well be for purposes of experimentation, to determine what value ranges of the variables with which he must deal are likely to be most sensitive for his study.

A model of this sort might be called, more specifically, a "function simulator." Any system which accomplishes a describable transformation, under known conditions, from a given input α to a specific and predictable output β, conceivably could be simulated in this fashion.[5] The function of a system which under given conditions produces β as output when presented with α as input is to transform α into β under those conditions. This function is simulated by a set of expressions which establish between variables x and y a relationship such that, for every value of x which is interpreted as representing an instance of α, there is associated a value of y which may be interpreted as representing the corresponding instance of β, under values of contributing variables which may be interpreted as representing the conditions under which the function transforms α into β. The strength of this approach to modeling is that the researcher may vary the relationships which he sets up among x and y and the contributing variables z and w, as demanded by the observed behavior of the system to be modeled, without being concerned with limiting himself to equations which are analytically solvable. The simulation technique thus combines the precision in expression and measurement of variables which is characteristic of a purely formal model with the ability to represent a wide range of functional interrelationships which is characteristic of some forms of replication.

2. It is not adventuresome to suggest that all material systems can be replicated. Since replicability often seems to be taken as a mark of a material thing, the statement that this is so is nearer to being a tautology than an empirical generalization. Molecules are replicated for purposes of classroom lectures in chemistry; and if they could not be replicated in this way (three-dimensionally) we

---

[5] As D. M. MacKay puts it, "any pattern of observable behaviour which can be specified in terms of unique and precisely-definable reactions to precisely-definable situations can in principle be imitated mechanically." See "Mindlike Behaviour in Artefacts," *The British Journal for the Philosophy of Science* (1951–1952), p. 108; reprinted in *The Modeling of Mind,* eds. Sayre and Crosson, pp. 228–229.

would feel that our concept of a molecule as an entity oc-
cupying space was somehow deficient. It is not necessary, of
course, that all features of an object be reproduced in order
for the reproduction to count as a replication, nor is it
necessary even that we be *able* to reproduce all features of
the object in the replication. But when we cannot reproduce *any* features of a thing in a material model, it seems
wrong to think of that thing as a material object. Thus an
electromagnetic state is not conceived as a material object.
It seems to be the case in general, rather, that we conceive
electromagnetic states (and quanta, and fields of energy) in
terms of formal models and not in terms of replications.
Nor is it necessary to have detailed or highly accurate
knowledge of a system in order to replicate it. Although a
replication based on inadequate knowledge is likely to be
defective, we would probably say in criticism of it that it is
not a good replication rather than that it is no replication
at all. Plato presumably had access to an armillary sphere
while composing the *Timeaus* which, despite our increased
knowledge of the solar system, we would still consider a
replication.[6]

Yet, although replication and simulation are distinct
procedures, there appears to be no good reason for disbe-
lieving that the function of any material system which can
be replicated is a function capable of being simulated. If
no other approach to simulation were available, it would
seem possible at least to increase the degree of detailed correspondence between the replication and its original until
the similarity in operation between the two systems is
matched by a similarity in results. The only limitation in
theory upon what can be simulated in the behavior of a
material system is imposed by our understanding of the

---

6 See *Plato's Cosmology*, by F. M. Cornford (New York, Harcourt, Brace
and Company, 1937), p. 74.

function performed by that system. Thus, for example, molecules which are understood well enough to be replicated might not be understood well enough to allow the chemist to simulate their combining action. Indeed, our inability to simulate the function of a material system normally would be taken as an indication that we do not understand that function fully. This limitation imposed by degree of understanding becomes even more crucial in the question of simulating mental functions. Let us now turn to this question.

We often speak of modeling processes and systems which would not be called "material" in any ordinary sense of the word. Thus the legal system or constitution of one country might be said to be modeled after that of another country. The curriculum of a university might be modeled after that of another; and a son might more or less deliberately imitate the mannerisms of his father. But when the question arises of constructing mechanical models of those aspects of human behavior which would normally be considered mental rather than strictly physical (e.g.,physiological or "behavioral"), the question becomes involved with emotionally-charged convictions that there are some talents which are in the unique possession of the human mind and which cannot in principle be duplicated by a "strictly mechanical" system. It is not within the scope of this essay to contribute to the worthwhile project of removing the emotion from this question. It might be a modest step in the right direction, however, to point out again that the problem of simulating mental behavior is quite different from the problem of replicating it. To replicate mental behavior would be to constitute a model which performs at least some of the same operations that the human brain performs in its behavior of thinking, perceiving, deciding, and so forth. Although some relatively crude and speculative replications of this sort already exist,[7] it seems unlikely on a technical basis alone that any results in this direction will be achieved in the foreseeable future which will change the traditional problem of the relation between mind and body from a conceptual to an empirical issue.

It is more pertinent, if we are to appreciate the remarkable potential of current computer technology for the modeling of human behavior, to restrict our attention specifically to the simulation of mental functions. The question whether some aspects of human mental behavior can be simulated is not speculative and, in fact, is no longer an open question. Behavior which most persons would be willing to consider typical of the human mind already has been simulated by essentially mechanical systems.[8] Let us attempt to clarify what it means to speak of the simulation of mental behavior.

Since the introduction of calculating machinery into the world of business, it is a standard concession that mere calculation is not a human prerogative. "But the discovery of mathematical proofs and theorems," it might be said by an imagined objector, "is quite another matter, one involving the exercise of a function of which man alone is capable. Machines will never be capable of this activity, any more than they will be capable of writing great music, understanding the subtleties of inspired poetry or discovering a basic scientific principle." This claim suggests something

---

[7] In a series of experiments with Perceptrons, Rosenblatt and his collaborators have attempted to reproduce in simplified form the very behavior exhibited by the neural networks of percipient organisms. A concise description of the purpose of these experiments is contained in "Analysis of Perceptrons," by H. D. Block, in *Proceedings of the Western Joint Computer Conference* (1961), pp. 281–289. It seems fair to say that the simulation of human perception is at best a secondary, and inadequately realized, goal of these experiments.

[8] See the Introduction to this book and Part II of *The Modeling of Mind*, eds. Sayre and Crosson.

which is probably true, but something which is obviously false as well. It probably is the case, as suggested above, that man will never confront a machine which reproduces exactly the operations by which he proves theorems, writes music or understands meanings. But it is the case at the same time that machines *can* be constructed which prove theorems, produce music and extract intelligible data from language. They do not accomplish these things in the same way that humans accomplish them. But they accomplish them nonetheless; and this is what is involved in the simulation of these human accomplishments.

Let us consider in more detail the example of proving a mathematical theorem. Grasping axioms and reasoning from these to a theorem, distinct from the axioms but related to them by a series of steps according to distinct rules of inference, is behavior of a type characteristic of a sophisticated human mind. In performing this function, the mind provides a transformation from the axioms to the theorems. The effect of the transformation is determined by the rules of inference. When a theorem is proposed which follows from the axioms according to the rules of inference, the mind's function in this regard has been discharged correctly. Now the operations which are involved in the performance of this function by the mind are not understood. But the function itself is understood, and has already been simulated on several separate occasions.[9] The function is to arrive at a theorem (the output) from axioms (the input) according to specific rules of inference which, when considered in this fashion, are the rules of transformation. Since it is a fortunate characteristic of mathematicians to insist upon precise articulation of their rules of inference, the task of constructing a machine to perform

---

[9] See, for example, H. Wang's "Toward Mechanical Mathematics," *IBM Journal of Research and Development* (January 1960); reprinted in *The Modeling of Mind*.

transformations of this sort generally is more or less routine, depending upon the complexity of the axioms and the rules of inference, and upon the "novelty" desired for the theorems to be proved.

In general, we may say that any mental function which is such that (1) its input and output can be specified with precision, and (2) the transformation it performs can be approximated by equations which express a determinate relationship between input and output, can for these reasons alone be simulated with some degree of adequacy. If, on the other hand, we do not have a clear understanding of either the input, the output, or the transformation, we will be unable to achieve an adequate simulation of that function. Our inability in such a case, however, reflects an inadequacy in human understanding, and is not a symptom of any "transcendence" of mental functions. Let us now consider in detail the ways in which lack of understanding of a function can block its successful simulation.

3. It is assumed for purposes of the present illustration that the term 'perceiving' designates a mental function with a specific input and a specific output, and that the input includes stimulation of the sort provided by properly operating sense organs. In addition to sensory stimulation, perceiving will be conceived also to constitute a response to deliverances of memory, and to the configurational aspects of sensory and memory data. These assumptions are not defended in this essay, and are mentioned here only to provide an intelligible example of the importance of conceptual clarity in the attempt to simulate mental functions.

Let 'F' represent the mental function of perceiving, 'x' an object of perception (the input to the function), and 'y' the behavior and behavior traits characteristic specifically of a person who has perceived x (the output of the function). Typical of such behavior traits might be a preference to avoid contact with x if such contact would be expected to be unpleasant, a tendency to respond affirmatively when asked if x is now visible, and an ability to focus one's attention on x when so directed. Consider the task of simulating the function F. When x and y are clearly defined, finding a transformation which will yield y when x is present is an experimental problem, towards the solution of which contributions might be expected from the experimental science of behavior. But if attempts to find a satisfactory transformation are unsuccessful, or if attempts to improve upon a partially adequate transformation persistently fail, the fault is not necessarily to be charged to the experimentalist. The reason for failure might be instead an inadequate conception of x. There might be unclarity about what features of x are relevant to the transformation between x and y, about how to characterize these features for purposes of simulating the transformation, or about the very structure of x itself insofar as it stands as an object of perception. There might be confusion as well regarding the type of function performed in perceptual behavior. Each of these would furnish an example of conceptual inadequacy, and any one of them would block a simulation attempt from likelihood of success.

An hypothetical example will illustrate how a faulty conception of x might preclude a successful simulation. If an experimentalist thinks of x, the object of perception, as a set of sensations localizable simultaneously with reference to the sense organs of a percipient, he will conceive the problem of simulating F as one of constructing a transformation which will require as an input a set of impulses corresponding to these sensations. Apart from the sheer technical difficulties of constructing a mechanical system which we would say is "responsive to sensations," or to impulses sufficiently similar to sensations to warrent identifying them with x, the fact is that an object of perception is different from a set of simultaneous sensations in several respects which are relevant to the perception of the object. First, some awareness of the structure of an object is usually part of our perception of it, and this structure is at least partially lost by analysis of an object into sensations associated with it when it is perceived. Second, objects of perception have histories, some awareness of which often enters into our perception of them, which cannot be identified with any set of simultaneous sensations. A third respect, related to this, is noted by Sluckin in his *Minds and Machines:* "A psychological examination of perception indicates that what is perceived depends not only upon the impact of stimuli from the outside world but also, most emphatically, upon the past experience of the perceiver," a factor which clearly cannot be represented by sensations associated with an object of present perception.[10] The experimenter may have his own reasons for representing x merely as a set of sensations. But when he does, he should not expect to achieve a satisfactory simulation of F.

Let us consider next the importance of having a clear conception of the function F itself. There are at least two respects in which a confused or inarticulate conception of a function can hinder its successful simulation: (a) it could lead one to construct a transformation which could never bear more than a gross resemblance to the function to be simulated; or (b) it could encourage the application of inappropriate criteria for judging the performance of the simulation system which, when failure is encountered, could result in our inability to isolate the factors which contribute most to the failure. These possibilities may be illustrated.

(a) Suppose that the human capacity which is exercised

---

10 *Minds and Machines,* by W. Sluckin (Pelican ed.; Baltimore, Penguin Books, Inc., 1960), p. 142.

when a physical object x is perceived is thought of as one which yields merely in an *identification* of x when x is presented as input. In this case, the task of simulating the human function of perception would be conceived as that of constructing a system which issues an affirmative response when x is present, and which issues a negative response or no response at all when x is not present to the system. But a system which performs only this function is a poor simulation of human perception, for it is characteristic that humans are capable of perceiving things which in fact they cannot identify. Moreover, humans sometimes simply fail to perceive objects which are "in full view" before them. Thus a human perceiver might respond in any of three ways when an object is presented for its perception: he may perceive and identify, he may perceive but not identify, or he may neither perceive nor identify. This function of human perception thus cannot be adequately simulated by a system which responds in only *one* way ("affirmatively") when an object x is presented to it as input.

(b) To illustrate the importance of appropriate criteria of success in an attempt to simulate a particular type of mental behavior, let us employ the example of recognition itself, and thereby anticipate certain results of the analysis in the following chapters. It is not unusual to find, in current literature on mechanical pattern-recognition, descriptions of attempts to simulate recognition of letter-inscriptions by systems which classify inscriptions according to their configurational or topological characteristics.[11] For example, a system might classify any configuration with two vertically-ordered closed loops as a B. Success of a classification system of this sort is judged according to percentage of "correct" classifications achieved during a series of tests with a prepared group of inscriptions. One recent

---

11 This is discussed more fully in Chapter Two.

attempt to classify inscriptions according to the way they can be fit with typical line segments of cursive script was reported to be 87 per cent successful, a rather high percentage as attempts of this sort have gone.[12]

Reports like this leave the impression that an adequate simulation of human recognition will be at hand when a classification system which yields 100 per cent correct results is finally achieved. This criterion of success is unsatisfactory for at least two reasons. For one, it is not clear what would be meant by talking about 100 per cent correct classification of letter-inscriptions. What is and what is not a B, to continue the example above, is what a person who knows the alphabet recognizes as B. But for many an inscription there is likely to be disagreement among people who know the alphabet as to whether it is or is not an inscription of a certain letter. The notion of a classification of inscriptions which is 100 per cent correct does not in itself *provide* a criterion. Rather, if it is to be meaningful, it *calls for* a criterion of what it is to be or not to be an inscription of a given letter. The second difficulty is a reflection of the fact that, however humans recognize specific letters of the alphabet, they do not do so with reference to configurational properties of letter-inscriptions alone. Whether a particular cursive inscription of the word 'boat' begins with a 'B' depends, not merely upon the shape of the first few line segments in the word, but upon whether the word conveys to a reader (*some* reader) the sense of the word 'boat'. This in turn depends upon a number of features of the written context and the reader's expectation, many of which at best could not be analyzed in terms of the mere configuration of the inscription.

---

[12] See "Machine Reading of Cursive Script," by L. S. Frishkopf and L. D. Harmon, in *Information Theory*, ed. Colin Cherry (London, Butterworth and Co., Ltd., 1961), p. 313. A commercial group, advertising in the *Scientific American* of March 1963 reports 98.5 per cent success for a somewhat similar endeavor.

Perfect performance of a classification system is not a satisfactory criterion of success in the simulation of human pattern-recognition, and the fact that this criterion is in common use belies a basic confusion between the concepts of classification and recognition. Although these concepts are related, in that a person who recognizes an object thereby will be able to classify it as an object of a certain sort, they remain fundamentally distinct in respects which we shall examine.

Further remarks in this direction are inappropriate until we have had a chance to consider in more detail various approaches which have been followed in the attempt to construct pattern-recognition mechanisms. To describe these approaches is the task of the following chapter. To criticize them constructively is the task of the remainder of the book.

CHAPTER TWO

MECHANICAL MODELS
OF RECOGNITION

1. The vision of a mixed society of human and artificial intelligence has stimulated men of imagination (besides science fictionists) ranging from theologians to behavioral scientists. The following quotation is from one of the latter.

As has been said in various ways, men are noisy, narrowband devices, but their nervous systems have very many parallel and simultaneously active channels. Relative to men, computing machines are very fast and very accurate, but they are constrained to perform only one or a few elementary operations at a time. Men are flexible, capable of "programming themselves contingently" on the basis of newly received information. Computing machines are singleminded, constrained by their "preprogramming." . . . To be rigorously correct, those characterizations would have to include many qualifiers. Nevertheless, the picture of dissimilarity (and therefore potential supplementation) that they present is essentially valid. Computing machines can do readily, well, and rapidly many things that are difficult or impossible for man, and men can do readily and well, though not rapidly, many things that are difficult or impossible for computers. That suggests that a symbiotic cooperation, if successful in integrating the positive characteristics of men and computers, would be of great value. The differences in speed and in language, of course, pose difficulties that must be overcome.[1]

Computing machines execute their instructions much more rapidly than men, and must be provided instructions in a symbolism which would never serve the ordinary purposes of human communication. This mismatch in speed and language poses severe problems for the efficient coupling of men and machines which are already well-known. Problems of one sort arise with the need for efficient human monitoring of mechanical operations in complex surveillance and control systems. A satisfactory air-traffic control system, for example, must be capable of dealing swiftly and effectively both with routine air-traffic situations and with unforeseeable situations in which mechanical operating routines are interrupted by periods of human control. Problems requiring human intervention can be detected by the computer within small fractions of a second. Having been referred to a human operator, however, such a problem often will require several minutes for its diagnosis and resolution. This inequity in rates of computer and of human performance is compounded by the fact that humans can be relied upon to handle only one problem at a time, whereas several problems requiring human attention might arise at any moment during operation of the system. In larger and more complex man-machine systems this often requires costly duplication and reduplication of human functions. One of the paradoxical facts of life with computer systems today is that more people often are required to monitor and to control the operation of a computer than have been replaced in routine data-processing tasks by the computer itself.

---

[1] This is from a prophetic article entitled "Man-Computer Symbiosis," by J. C. R Licklider, in *IRE Transactions of Human Factors in Electronics* (March 1960), p. 6.

Problems of another sort arise even with the more routine business and research applications of smaller data-processing systems. Once computers have been instructed by their human users, they can carry out their instructions with rapidity and with low probability of error. But the task of preparing instructions for a computer can take several months, and often requires considerable human ingenuity. Then after an adequate set of instructions has been prepared, more time often is required to enter the instructions into the machine than will be required for their execution once the machine begins to operate. This problem, in turn, is complicated by the fact that any data or intermediate instructions needed by a computer during its actual operation must be prepared and entered by the same time-consuming techniques as were employed in giving the machine its initial instructions.

Among various ways in which problems like these might be reduced, one of the most intriguing is to make computers responsive to a natural language. This is one practical motivation behind the extensive research effort today to devise effective pattern-recognition mechanisms. Both written and spoken letter-symbols exhibit patterns to which humans normally respond both rapidly and reliably. If computers could be made to respond to the same patterns in a similar way, the communications gap between machines and people might be narrowed considerably. Computers with a facility of this sort not only could alleviate many problems of military command and control, but moreover could read and process our millions of income tax returns and could make the comprehensive automatic mail sorter dreamed about in the Post Office Department a reality. Such a machine could perform routine tasks of information retrieval and collation for doctors, lawyers and scholars. When coupled with an automatic typing device, a computer which could "understand" spoken language could produce an accurately typed letter within seconds of dictation. And a reliable reader of variously formed written letters could be developed into a valuable reading machine for the blind.

The possibility of a mechanical pattern-recognition system also has attracted considerable attention from the point of view of theoretical studies of sensory perception. A great deal might be learned about human perception if a machine could be built which performs approximately the same functions in a way more accessible to study than the human nervous system. Just as the aeronautical engineer has his wind tunnel, so might the physiologist, the biologist and the psychologist be provided with their own experimental model if the function of human pattern-recognition could be reproduced within a mechanical system based upon an electronic computer.

Our concern in this book is on a more modest scale, for it stems from the entirely practical problem of preparing a machine to recognize letter-symbols written in script by a human hand. The purpose of this chapter is to review some of the more promising techniques thus far devised for the accomplishment of such a device. Since all of the techniques to be discussed involve digital computers, we begin with a very brief survey of some of the operating features of these machines which, on the one hand, make the task of pattern-recognition difficult but, on the other, make it at least possible.

2. Our current electronic computers share their ancestry with the mechanical desk calculators common in business offices.[2] This ancestry traces directly back to the

---

[2] The discussion here and in parts of Chapter Three is patterned after "Human and Mechanical Recognition," in *Methodos*, XIV (1962); reprinted in *The Modeling of Mind*, eds. Kenneth Sayre and Frederick Crosson (Notre Dame, University of Notre Dame Press, 1963). Extensive revisions have been made, however, and some former claims have been retracted.

difference engines of Charles Babbage (about 1820), and indirectly to calculating mechanisms built by Pascal and Leibniz. Yet the major developments which separate the electronic computer from the desk calculator have taken place within the past twenty-five years.

In Babbage's engine, as well as in the desk calculator, each number entered into the machine is represented by the position or orientation of one or several mechanical components. In a simple machine two adjacent wheels with numerical two's displayed on top might indicate the number twenty-two: yet it would be the position of the wheels rather than what happened to be marked on them that would represent the number in the machine. Calculations in such a machine would occur in motions of interconnected physical parts. Thus the operating speed of such a machine is limited by the speed with which its components can be moved, and its information-handling capacity is limited by the physical constraints involved in the efficient mechanical connection of a large number of distinct physical parts.

Computer technology in the contemporary sense was made possible by the substitution of electronic storage and switching devices for the cogs and levers of the calculating machine. Previously an item of information could be represented within a machine only by mechanical states of its components. It became possible now to represent information in terms of the momentary electromagnetic states of vacuum tubes. Since vacuum tube states can be altered very rapidly, the operating speed of these machines was greatly increased. But the information-handling capacity of the early electronic computers was severely limited by the technical problem of dissipating the heat energy resulting from the simultaneous operation of the large number of vacuum tubes needed to represent a large number of separate bits of information. This particular restriction was overcome only recently by the development of electronic storage devices other than vacuum tubes, and by the invention of small solid state electronic switching and amplifying devices which perform most of the functions of vacuum tubes more quickly and with less energy dissipation. With these devices incorporated into contemporary computers, both storage and speed capabilities have been extended by several orders of magnitude over corresponding capabilities of the older machines.

One primary measure of a computer's information-handling capacity is the number of two-state electromagnetic units within its circuitry set aside for storage of data and operating instructions. The programmer is trained to think of these units as grouped together into blocks (usually called "words") which provide the basis of communication between the computer and its users. In a given computer, each "word" consists of a fixed number of units (for example, thirty-two), and each word is provided a unique designation or "address" in terms of which it can be referred to by the programmer and by the control section of the computer itself during actual operation. While in theory there need be no specific limit to the number of words available for data storage in most computers, considerations of price and size make a capacity of 60,000 to 70,000 words very respectable for the larger machines in current use. For applications in which demands on a computer's storage exceed what is provided within the machine itself, its storage can be expanded without limit by the addition of peripheral equipment such as magnetic tapes and revolving drums which can be addressed by the control section of the computer with special programming instructions. The disadvantage of any peripheral storage facility is that much more time is required on the average to retrieve data from it than from internal storage areas. All computers further have provisions whereby an operator can enter data directly into the machine, either before or during actual operation. As we have seen, however, access involving human manipulations consumes a great deal of time relative to the operating speed of the computer itself. The extreme speed of the computer is used to best advantage if all necessary data can be represented within the machine before actual operation begins.

Part of the storage facilities of a typical general-purpose computer is reserved for instructions formulated with reference to the user's particular application. These instructions set up a sequence of operations which as an end result produce the information desired by the user. Instructions of this sort are administered through the control section of the computer, the function of which is to determine at each stage in the process what specific operation is required at the immediately following stage. The control section is capable of changing the location of the contents of any word within the system and of performing basic arithmetical or logical operations upon the contents of any one or several words. In some computers the control section is capable moreover of altering some of its own operating instructions. This latter facility, as we shall see, makes possible a particularly powerful approach to mechanical pattern-recognition. When this facility is present, the programmer can issue instructions which have the effect of allowing the computer itself to alter parts of its instructions in a stepwise fashion until it hits upon a particularly favorable way of handling a given problem. In such an application, the programmer must provide both instructions for a systematic alteration of the machine's procedures and a criterion by which the relative merits of alternative procedures can be tested, but he need not be able to foresee all procedures which the computer will test as it works its way towards the desired set of operating procedures.

The term 'peripheral equipment' generally is taken to refer, not only to equipment such as tape units and magnetic drums which provide auxiliary storage facilities, but also to the various devices which implement communication between the computer and its users. A further distinction is made between input equipment, by which data and instructions are entered into the central computer, and output equipment, by which results of the computer's operation are returned to the user. There is a wide variety of possible equipment of either sort, since any mechanical means of data acquisition or transfer could be used to provide an entry into the computer and any mechanical display system with a sufficient number of discriminable states could be used to exhibit its results. Commonly used input devices include punched card and magnetic tape "readers," telephone receivers and various push-button control panels. Among more common output devices are card punches, magnetic tape "writers," telephonic transmitters and various visual display systems such as automatic typewriters, line-printers and oscilloscopes. Each input device must be connected to the computer in such a way that information presented to it is transformed in terms of a sequence of binary states, in which form it can be entered directly into the storage section of the computer. And each output device must be capable of receiving information expressed in sequences of binary states and of transforming it unambiguously into a means of representation directly intelligible to a trained operator. In short, all terms of communication between the computer and its users must at some stage be represented by unique series of binary states. Since a series of this sort in itself bears no intelligible content, the user must share with the computer an explicit set of conventions by means of which each series of binary states correctly generated by the computer will represent some particular instruction or datum, or in general some particular bit of information. To learn the conventions of meaningful representations within a given computer is an important part of learning how that particular machine operates.

The main point to be retained from this cursory survey is a general one regarding the way information is entered into, stored and handled by digital computers. Any item of information, whether a number, an instruction or a rule of operation, must be represented within the computer in a form which will enable it to have the desired effect upon the machine's operation. This representation must be in the form of binary states of electronic or electromagnetic elements. In order to achieve this representation, the user must communicate with the computer in terms of a specially devised language which provides explicit conventions for locating and processing information of each specific sort within the computer itself. Although many auxiliary devices have been developed to help the user communicate with the machine, the result of communication in each case is the representation within the computer of each item of information in terms of particular states of its binary components.

Thus there is a sense in which what we can instruct a computer to do is limited by the capabilities of the machine. We cannot instruct it to perform functions which are intrinsically incapable of being expressed entirely in terms of the computer's special language of binary states. From another point of view, however, this feature of digital computers might be construed as reflecting a possible limitation on the part of the user himself. We cannot instruct a computer to perform a function which *we* do not know how to express adequately in terms of the language of the machine. Our assumption, as we continue to seek ways of developing effective mechanical pattern-recognition systems, is that our inability thus far to produce such a system is due to a limitation of the latter and not of the former sort.

3. In a chapter entitled "Cybernetics and Cognition" of his book *Cognition,* F. H. George comments upon the suggestion that human perception is dependent upon some form of classification, which he remarks "is the same essential principle on which the input of the digital computer operates. . . ."[3] In a summary statement he says:

> Looking back at what was said about perception in earlier chapters, we can see that the principle of classification is consistent with what we know about the process of perception. By this we mean that recognition can be understood in general terms as that of classifying (or categorizing) subjects into sets, whereby we simply have the problem of saying what the probability is that a particular subset "belongs to" a particular set. This is the basic manner in which all the special senses might work, although many complicating factors connected with the particular structure of the special senses may be expected to obscure the simple notion of classification.[4]

One of the main burdens of the present essay is to clarify and to establish a concept of recognition according to which the statement quoted must be judged incorrect in several respects. It must be admitted, however, that almost every writer on the topic of mechanical pattern-recognition who has made any attempt to articulate his opinion agrees with the author of this statement that recognition can properly be understood as a form of classification. The task of the present section is to review several of the more promising techniques which have been developed for achieving a pattern-recognition mechanism.

---

[3] F. H. George, *Cognition* (London, Methuen & Co., Ltd., 1962), p. 212.

[4] *Ibid.* For a comparably explicit assimilation of the concepts of recognition and of classification on the part of a psychologist, see H. A. Binder's "A Statistical Model for the Process of Visual Recognition," *Psychological Review* (1955), pp. 119–129.

Let us begin accordingly with a brief preliminary analysis of the concept of classification.

Any group of objects which have a property (simple or complex) in common constitutes a class which can be defined with reference to that property. All objects which possess that property, and only such objects, are admissible as members of that class. The property which defines a given class thus both qualifies an object which possesses it for membership in the class and distinguishes (in definition if not in extension) that class from all other classes. Let us use the term 'invariant' to refer to the defining property of a class.

Now the procedure of classification is one in which an object is associated in some way with a specific class or in which each of a group of objects is associated individually with one of several alternative classes. The classification is correct if and only if each object possesses the property which is the invariant of the class with which it is associated. In order to determine whether an object has been classified correctly, it is necessary of course to determine whether the object has the property which is the invariant of the appropriate class.

There are at least two sorts of problems which might arise in the attempt to classify a group of objects. For one, there may be a problem of determining whether a given object in fact has the property which is the invariant of a specific class. In such a case there would be no problem regarding *what* property is the invariant of the class concerned. Another sort of problem arises when one has reason to think there is an invariant which associates a given group of objects into a class, but is unable to determine precisely what that invariant is. The task of achieving mechanical recognition of letter-patterns brings up problems of both sorts. There is the problem, first, of determining what features of a given class of letter-inscriptions (for example, inscriptions of A) serve as the invariant of that class. And second, there is the problem of devising mechanical techniques for detecting these features when they occur in individual inscriptions. These problems often merge in practice, but as we shall see in the following chapter it is the first that leads to most serious difficulty.

Many different approaches to the problem of providing invariants for the mechanical recognition of letter-patterns have been explored by computer technologists, and a few have been tested by incorporating them in actual computer programs. It would be tedious and for our purposes unrewarding to attempt to describe even the more successful of these individually. Let us instead discuss three general approaches to the problem, some one or more of which can be recognized in practically every system thus far reported in the literature. We shall discuss in order the methods (1) of template matching, (2) of description and (3) of segmentation.

The method of *template matching* provides a workable technique for identifying inscriptions of letter-patterns which are relatively uniform in size, shape and orientation. This technique holds no promise for the recognition of variously formed letter-inscriptions of human writers, which is our main concern in this essay, but a brief discussion of it will help us understand better the advantages and shortcomings of alternative techniques. We will assume that each inscription to be recognized is positioned initially in a photoelectric scanner which is capable of discriminating small light and dark areas, and which is connected to a computer in such a way that a unique location in the computer's storage corresponds to each small area discriminated by the scanner. Each dark area may be represented in the computer by an electromagnetic charge interpretable as 'yes', and each light area by a charge interpretable as 'no'. In preparation for its recognition task, the computer will be provided with a standard figures with which to compare the presented inscription. This standard figure also is represented in the computer by an ordered series of yes's and no's, enabling it to be directly compared with the inscription to be tested. If all yes's and no's of the standard figure correspond respectively to yes's and no's of the presented inscription, the computer indicates that the inscription has been determined to be one of the same type as the standard. If there are few correspondences, a response occurs signifying no recognition. As a rule, however, neither of these extreme cases will occur. Since even carefully formed inscriptions often deviate considerably from any chosen standard, each inscription tested will correspond less than perfectly with the standard figure. The human director of the recognition program thus must decide in advance what degree of correspondence is necessary to warrant an affirmative response by the computer.

In the method of *description* any feature or set of features of a pattern which can be described in the language of the computer is a possible candidate for being the invariant of that pattern. When a particular set of features has been selected as invariant, the problem of the programmer is to devise some means of detecting the presence or absence of those features in particular inscriptions presented to the recognition system. Since these features are usually properties of shape or topology which can be mathematically defined, the practical task of the programmer is one of providing formulae the applicability or inapplicability of which to the inscription indicates the presence or absence of the features in question. Two generally distinct ways of testing for the presence of such features have been proposed. One involves processing the inscription, as it is presented to the recognition system, in order to determine whether the features in question can be distinguished from other features of the inscription which are inessential for the pattern to be recognized. The other way involves the independent generation of line segments with known features, and a subsequent test to determine whether these segments can be matched with features of the inscription to be identified. If the correspondence between the inscription and the features of a certain set of generated segments is sufficiently close, the inscription is identified as a member of the class, the invariant of which is defined by those features.[5] The latter approach is surely more promising. The reasons for this, however, cannot be made clear until the final chapter, at which place it will be appropriate to discuss this approach in more detail.

The most difficult problem in employing the method of description has been that of determining which characteristics of shape and topology are pertinent for distinguishing among the various letters of the alphabet. Among features which have been exploited in actual research with this method are closure, concavity, curvature or straightness of side, and various characteristics of edges and corners. One researcher lists thirty-two features which in some combination figure as invariants in his recognition program.[6] But the great latitude of choice of invariants provided by this approach introduces its own problems. Since any consistent combination of features can serve as an invariant, the number of invariants the researcher might want to examine to determine the most suitable combina-

[5] One of the best examples of this approach to date is in some remarks by Murray Eden in "Handwriting and Pattern Recognition," *IRE Transactions on Information Theory* (February 1962), and in "The Characterization of Cursive Writing" by Murray Eden and Morris Halle, in *Information Theory,* ed. Colin Cherry (London, Butterworth and Co., Ltd., 1961).

[6] S. H. Unger, "Pattern Detection and Recognition," *Proceedings of the IRE,* XLVII (October 1959), 1737–1752.

tion for identifying a particular pattern could be excessive. For some applications, like programming a computer to play ticktacktoe with circles and crosses, the relevant invariants are more or less apparent. In other applications some arbitrary choice of invariants might be acceptable. But when the researcher's hope is to produce a machine which approaches human performance in recognizing poorly formed letter-inscriptions, the proper choice of invariants is neither apparent nor arbitrary. Rather than undertake the pointless task of trying all possible combinations of features present in the inscriptions he wishes the machine to identify, it is natural that the researcher should enlist the aid of the computer itself in determining which combination will work best. This can be done by an application of what might be called "the principle of the self-optimizing system."

Any system which has a specific function to perform is capable of undergoing qualitative improvement or degradation in its performance, as measured by some applicable criterion. When the performance of a system cannot be further improved under specific conditions of operation, the system is said to have been "optimized" under those conditions. A system might be optimized either by external control of its operation or by alterations originating within the system itself. Thus a system which moves from an inoptimal to an optimal state without direct external control over its operations might be said to be capable of self-optimization. As we have seen, a capability of this sort can be incorporated in some digital computers by provisions for alteration of their own operating instructions on the basis of previous successes and failures in a given task. This capability provides a technique which has been employed with considerable enthusiasm to the problem of providing invariants for the recognition of letter-inscriptions.

The programmer's initial part in the process of self-optimization is to supply the machine with a list of features in terms of which inscriptions presented to it can be characterized, and to prepare a routine whereby the computer might test various combinations of these features in an attempt to find an adequate characterization of a given pattern. The invariants with which the machine begins its recognition attempts will be generated randomly, and generally will be unsuccessful. As "learning" progresses, however, those features which enter into partially successful combinations will be given higher probabilities of recurring in other combinations. At the completion of the "learning" phase, the computer should have evolved a set of features which, when taken as the invariant of a given letter-pattern, should provide for the highest percentage of correct identifications of that pattern within the system's capability. The programmer's main contribution to this desired result is to provide a set of operating instructions which insures that any change the computer makes in its set of invariants will tend towards the optimal combination of features.[7]

Although this technique of self-optimization has been applied most frequently in conjunction with the method of description, there seems to be no reason why it might not be applied also in conjunction with some form of the method of template-matching briefly described above. In-

---

[7] For examples of this approach, see (1) O. G. Selfridge, "Pandemonium: a Paradigm for Learning," *Proceedings of a Symposium on Mechanisation of Thought Processes,* II (London, Her Majesty's Stationery Office, 1959); (2) D. M. MacKay, "The Epistemological Problem for Automata," *Automata Studies,* eds. C. E. Shannon and J. McCarthy (Princeton, Princeton University Press, 1956); or (3) T. Marill and D. M. Green, "Statistical Recognition Functions and the Design of Pattern Recognizers," *IRE Transactions on Electronic Computers* (December 1960). Among problems remaining to be solved for the entirely successful use of such an approach are how to bring the machine to an optimal combination of features in a relatively brief time, and how to insure that the program does not develop towards a good but not an optimal combination and in the process lose its path towards the one optimal combination.

stead of matching an entire letter-pattern with a pre-arranged template, this application would require breaking the patterns to be identified down into "sub-patterns" to which the computer could respond in various combinations. In preparation for the task of determining the invariants of the various patterns to be identified by the computer system, the programmer would supply several "basic" configurations some combination of which he would hope to match uniquely with each of the patterns in question. In "learning" to identify one of these patterns, the computer would begin by applying several possible combinations selected at random. In response to information about the success and failure of these preliminary attempts, the computer would alter its own instructions to give a higher probability of further occurrence to those "sub-patterns" present most frequently in the more successful attempts. The result of a successful application of this method then would be an invariant in terms of "sub-patterns" which would serve for the identification of each of the letter-patterns to which the system was prepared to respond.[8]

---

[8] A system which seems to fit this general description is reported by Uhr and Vossler in "A Pattern Recognition Program that Generates, Evaluates and Adjusts its Own Operators," *Proceedings of the Western Joint Computer Conference*, XIX (1961). The first step in their procedure is to present the pattern to be identified in a square 400 binary cell matrix and to mask out all unoccupied cells beyond the periphery of the pattern. Next, "the input pattern is transformed into four 3-bit characteristics by each of a set of 5×5 matrix operators, each cell of which may be visualized as containing either a 0, 1, or blank. These small matrices which measure local characteristics of the pattern are translated, one at a time, across and then down that part of the matrix which lies within the mask. The operator is considered to match the input matrix whenever the 0's and 1's in the operator correspond to identical values in the pattern, and for each match the location of the center cell of the 5×5 matrix operator is temporarily recorded (p. 556)." Insofar as these operators can be conceived as "sub-patterns," this system seems generally to fit our description above. A notable feature of Uhr and Vossler's system, as the title of their paper suggests, is that the system can be prepared to generate its own operators in response to the demands of a particular identification problem. A summary of the principles of operation of this system is provided by E. B. Hunt in Chapter 9 of *Concept Learning* (New York, John Wiley and Sons, 1963).

The third approach to be mentioned here is that of *segmentation*, thus far explored in the literature by only a few writers and by them only in a cursory fashion.[9] This approach bears an obvious resemblance to that discussed in the paragraph above, but has the notable advantage of suggesting that handwriting might be conceived as a form of encoding and that letter-recognition consequently might be conceived as a form of decoding.[10] Instead of analyzing patterns to be identified by the machine in terms of "subpatterns," this approach involves breaking the line formations of these patterns down into discrete segments. Identification of a given pattern then would be accomplished with reference to the combination of segments present within it.[11] Murray Eden's attempts in the direction of this approach provide an illustration.[12] The basic elements in Eden's system are four symbols, mathematically defined, called "bar," "hook," "arch" and "loop." Each letter to be identified (Eden deals with both lower and upper case letter notations) is analyzed in terms of ordered sequences of these elements. One of the "shorter" letter-patterns is that of the lower case J, consisting of a "bar" followed by a "loop"; the "longest" letter-pattern is that of the upper case M, consisting of a sequence of ten "bars"

---

9 See "The Characterization of Cursive Writing," by Eden and Halle, in *Information Theory*, ed. Colin Cherry, pp. 287–299; and "Handwriting and Pattern Recognition" in *IRE Transactions on Information Theory*, pp. 160–166. In some respects, the system attributed to L. D. Harmon in "Machine Reading of Cursive Script," by L. S. Frishkopf and L. D. Harmon, in *Information Theory*, pp. 300–316, can also be grouped under this heading. In this latter connection, note the remarks by R. L. Grimsdale in the discussion at the end of that paper.

10 This remark is elucidated in Part Four, the contents of which are independent of any application of this technique cited in current literature.

11 The "sub-patterns" of the previous approach are not segments of the over-all pattern. A printed capital H, for example, manifests numerous "sub-patterns," among them a three-sided figure open on the top, a three-sided figure open at the bottom, the figure of a chair viewed from the side facing left, the figure of a chair similarly viewed facing right, etc. But this printed H is naturally segmented only into three parts: the vertical line to the left, the vertical line to the right, and the horizontal line in the middle.

12 *Loc. cit.*

and "arches" uniquely ordered. The task of the recognition mechanism in this system is to construct sequences of elements which when combined can be matched with letter-patterns presented to the system for identification. The procedure for determining correctness of match is described by Eden as follows:[13]

> First, a subject is asked to write a letter. It is then inserted in some appropriate format into the computer. The computer output consists of some symbol standing for one of the finite set of letter equivalence classes. Finally, the subject is asked whether the identification is correct or, more usually, the operator of the experiment determines whether the computer's output agrees with the subject's input. . . . Identification by a generative procedure leads to a clear definition of the set of permissible patterns. The class of acceptable patterns is simply that set which can be generated by the rules operating on the primitive symbols of the theory.

It should be mentioned that Eden conceives his system in the stage in which it was reported to be of interest primarily as one for generating and not for identifying letter-patterns, in which latter capacity it had not yet been tested.[14]

As is apparent from the quotation, even the sophisticated approach of Eden is dominated by the concept of recognition as a form of classification. Let us now summarize various common aspects of the techniques discussed above.

4. Features of existing methods for the mechanical recognition of letter-patterns to which reference will be made during the remainder of this discussion are (1) that the programmer of the system must provide the basic categories in terms of which the pattern to be identified is described within the system; (2) that the procedure of

---

[13] "Handwriting and Pattern Recognition," *op. cit.*, p. 161.
[14] *Ibid.*, p. 166.

identification requires analysis of the input pattern into components ("sub-patterns" or segments) which is accomplished independently of the actual identification; and (3) that the procedure of recognition or identification is conceived as one of classifying the various patterns presented to the system. The only exception to (1) which we have noted is with the system of Uhr and Vossler, where the computer is empowered to generate its own "operators." These "operators" in turn, however, are describable only in terms of states of the elements of the matrix in which they are applied to the input pattern. The only exception to (2) is with a straightforward application of the template-matching technique first discussed above, a method notably inadequate for the identification of the varying characters of handwritten script. The feature of current systems most worthy of note, however, is the third. Apparently without exception, the problem of achieving mechanical recognition of handwritten letters has been conceived as one of providing an invariant for each letter-pattern in the alphabet, with reference to which any inscription of that pattern can be recognized as such. Attempts have been made to describe suitable invariants with reference to various features of shape or topology of the over-all pattern, or with reference to spatial or topological features of elements within the over-all patterns. But the feasibility of approaching pattern-recognition as a problem of classification has not been questioned.

In the following chapter it is argued that there are certain prominent aspects of pattern-recognition in human beings which we cannot duplicate in mechanical systems as long as we conceive recognition as merely a form of classification. The task of showing that recognition in fact cannot be conceived correctly as a form of classification is left for the chapters which follow. Let us turn now to examine some consequences of this mistaken conception.

CHAPTER THREE

A CONCEPTUAL
IMPASSE

1. The notion that recognition is a form of classification has practical consequences. Guided by it, our efforts to simulate human letter-recognition are directed towards a particular sort of classification mechanism. We feel that the simulation of human letter-recognition will be accomplished when, and only when, we succeed in constructing a machine which is capable of classifying correctly, according to alphabetic type, every letter-symbol with which it is presented.

Now in order to prepare a machine to classify letter-symbols as being of a certain type, one must be able to specify those characteristics which distinguish between symbols of that type and others excluded by it. Thus we have been led to think that the primary problem in the simulation of letter-recognition is one of isolating those characteristics of the symbols to be recognized with reference to which they can be correctly and unambiguously classified by a machine. Since letter-symbols are commonly conceived as essentially spatial configurations, the characteristics which might provide criteria for correct classification are usually sought among the various spatial features of the symbols in question.

Thus there is no occasion for surprise in the fact that even the more sophisticated letter-recognition techniques discussed in the last chapter are basically methods of classification with reference to criteria of shape or of other spatial characteristics. The problem of applying these techniques is that of providing an invariant for each class of symbol to be recognized. We thus encounter the puzzling question of what features, if any, there may be present in a given letter-symbol which make the difference between its being that particular symbol and its being a symbol for some other letter or not being a letter-symbol at all.

One approach to the problem of finding criteria for classifying letter-symbols which at first seems natural is to determine what characteristics contribute to the recognition of these symbols by human beings. But this has proven not to be an easy task, even with such apparently simple letter-patterns as those of the written A, M or T. Normally we encounter no difficulty in recognizing inscriptions of these patterns, but we find that we have only the most tentative suggestions about how we are able to recognize these inscriptions and to distinguish them from others. As we reflect upon the problem, it appears not only that the criteria which might operate in human letter-recognition are surprisingly obscure but, moreover, that there are reasons to think that recognition in some cases is accomplished without reference to any criteria at all. These reasons will be examined shortly. The result, however, is that the would-be simulator of human letter-recognition is left in an impasse. Under his conception of recognition as a form of classification, he finds himself unable to understand how human letter-recognition is even possible and unable to discern in what direction he should move to increase his chances of achieving an adequate simulation. He is unable to find adequate criteria for classifying the various symbols which are to be recognized mechanically. Yet so long as he is dominated by the notion that recognition is a form of classification, he can think of no other approach to the simulation task.

This impasse is of a conceptual nature, for it stems from an inadequate notion of the very behavior we are attempting to simulate. The fact of that matter is that we do not have a clear conception of what counts as recognition of a letter-symbol by a human being, and consequently that we are not clear about what sort of behavior is supposed to be simulated by a letter-recognition mechanism. It follows that we cannot have a clear conception about how an adequate simulation of this behavior might be achieved. Let us state at the outset that the conceptual deficiency in question is not the admitted lack of a precise and comprehensive psychological explanation of recognition. It is rather the lack of a precise and defensible conception of what humans *do* in situations which would serve as typical instances of letter-recognition.

There is no attempt in this chapter to remove this conceptual deficiency, or to overcome the impasse to which it commits the would-be simulator of human recognitive behavior. This undertaking is left for the remainder of the essay. Our concern for the moment rather is to explore the conceptual outlines of the impasse more fully. The justification for this exploration is simple. Unless we are quite clear about what aspects of human letter-recognition are eluding our simulation attempts, we cannot hope to remedy our current inability to construct mechanical recognition systems with a versatility approaching that of human beings.

2. Although recognition is not a form of classification, it does not follow from this alone that human recognition of letter-symbols cannot be simulated by some sort

of classifying mechanism. To simulate a function is not necessarily to replicate it, and in some cases it may be feasible to simulate an activity of a given sort on the basis of a mechanism which performs in an entirely different fashion. Thus, for example, the composition of music has been simulated by a computer system in which sequences of musical elements are generated randomly and then are separated according to principles of aesthetic coherence and interest. Here the creative act of composition is simulated by a process which is essentially analytic; and there is as much difference between composition and analysis as between building a house and sorting old lumber. So it remains at least an open possibility that human recognition can be simulated on the basis of a mechanism constructed explicitly for purposes of classification.

Such an approach in fact is notably unpromising. But to see why this is the case, we should be aware of certain features of human recognition which are not immediately obvious and which at first may seem a bit paradoxical.

In this and the following section we shall see reasons to believe (1) that people often are able to recognize objects, the identifying characteristics of which they cannot specify, and (2) that people are capable of learning to recognize objects, the identifying characteristics of which cannot be expressed in terms of features with which previously they were familiar. Consequences of these two facts, with regard to the feasibility of simulating letter-recognition with classifying mechanisms, are drawn in the last two sections of this chapter.

Although recognition is not classification, it clearly is the case that when a person has recognized an object as being of a certain sort he is able thereby to classify the object accordingly. Thus to recognize a bird as a finch enables one to classify the bird as a finch, and to recognize a mark as a letter-symbol enables one to classify it as such. But given the ability to classify an object thus obtained, it does not follow that the person who recognizes the object necessarily will be able to specify characteristics of the object with reference to which he might claim to have recognized it. Paradoxical as this might seem at first glance, it is in fact the case that we often are able to recognize objects without being able to specify any characteristics by which they might be unambiguously identified. Consider the typical case (a) below, in which a person is able to recognize a written letter-symbol without being able to say precisely by what features it can be identified.

Case (a). A human observer is presented with a series of written symbols, some but not all of which are instances of the letter D.[1] No two of the symbols which are instances of D have exactly the same shape, nor have they any topological features in common. Some contain only one loop (d), others contain two (ɗ), while yet others (ꝺ) contain no loop at all; some contain a straight line (d), others none (ꝺ); some (ɖ) but not others (ɗ) contain discontinuities in their inscription; etc.[2] None of these D's, however, is particularly distorted. Although the observer is able to recognize each of these letter-symbols without hesitation, he is not able to say precisely what they all have in common by way of spatial characteristics. Let us generalize this example. It seems sufficiently clear that a set of symbols meeting these conditions could be provided such that a large majority of persons literate in the Roman alphabet would identify the same symbols as instances of D and would reject all others. Yet few of these persons, if any, would be prepared to specify characteristics of the

---

1 A distinction between letter-token and letter-type is drawn in Chapter Ten. A letter-token is a physical object representing one of twenty-six letter-types in our alphabet. Case (a) concerns letter-tokens.

2 These examples are drawn from Plates 4, 7, 13 and 33 of *A Book of Scripts,* by Alfred Fairbank, in the *King Penguin Books* series (Baltimore, Penguin Books, Inc., 1949).

chosen symbols which might have served as criteria by which they made their choices. If, indeed, it were a routine matter to specify necessary and sufficient characteristics by which instances of the written letter D could be identified, it would be a relatively routine matter to construct a machine which could perform this identification.

There are other objects besides letter symbols which we can recognize with high reliability, but for which no identifying characteristics can be specified. One type of example concerns unanalyzable qualities such as red, sweetness or pleasure. By 'red' in this example, we should understand a quality of which a person is directly aware and not the physical occurrences (e.g., light of certain wavelengths) which may have occasioned his awareness of the quality. The light normally associated with the experience of red can be identified in terms of measurements by a spectrometer. But red as a quality directly experienced by a person is not a complex property, and hence cannot be identified in terms of other properties or occurrences. Thus our recognition of red must proceed without involvement of a set of identifying criteria.

In a sense, however, red is not a pattern, and our main concern is with the recognition of patterns. An alternative example is provided by configurations of radar returns on a display scope which represent moving aircraft. An experienced radar operator usually can distinguish without difficulty configurations which correspond to moving aircraft from those caused by anomalous radar returns, while in similar instances an unexperienced observer would be unable to see any difference between these configurations. Yet it seems impossible in fact, if not in principle, to formulate any set of characteristics which are shared by all aircraft returns and which are at least partly missing from all anomalous configurations.

Another suggestive example is the "puzzle" consisting

of a maze of lines and shadows which conceal the visual image of an ordinary object. Once the object is "seen" in the scramble, it stands out clearly and can be recognized easily in subsequent viewings of the maze. Yet a quantitative description of the lines and shadows within the maze after the object had been identified would not differ in any obvious way from a similar description of these features as they appeared prior to identification of the object. That is, a description of the arrangement of lines of the picture in which the object is recognizable will not differ from a description of the arrangement of lines of the picture in which the object does not appear. Criteria for identification of the object thus cannot be given merely in terms of the shape of the object as it appears in the maze.

Case (b). There are other objects which we often recognize without reference to identifying characteristics, but which are such that characteristics for identifying them would be relatively easy to specify. For example, we are able to recognize square figures as squares without counting sides, and without any conscious reference to a definition of the square which makes explicit its property of having four straight sides. And a five-pointed star often can be recognized as such without explicit counting of the points. In such cases it is possible to apply specific criteria in identifying the object, but usually we are able to recognize the object without explicit reference to criteria.

Case (c). There are yet other cases in which identification of an object does seem necessarily to involve reference to some set of distinguishing characteristics. In particular, the identification of objects whose relevant characteristics cannot be taken in at a glance requires application of identifying criteria. Recognition of a 1,000-sided figure, or of an extended proof in logic, requires deliberate reference to defining properties of the object to be recognized. If one cannot assess the specific features required of a proper

logical proof, he cannot identify a proper proof when con-
fronted with one; if one cannot count, he cannot identify
a 1,000-sided figure. In such cases, there is generally no
question of recognition without reference to defining
characteristics.

Cases (a) and (b) have in common that no explicit set
of criteria figures in the recognition of the object in question. Only in Case (c) does reference to a set of identifying
criteria appear essential. In Case (b), identifying characteristics could be supplied but are not essential for recognition, while in Case (a) no common characteristics appear
available to serve as identifying criteria. Although the
primary problem of this essay is located with Case (a), our
present concern is to explore various respects in which human recognition differs from any classification procedure
which could be duplicated mechanically. It will be helpful
to consider further relevant aspects of those cases in which
human identification of objects depends upon or could be
supplemented by reference to classificatory criteria.

3. In cases where criteria for identification figure,
either explicitly or implicitly, there is a further distinction
to be made between ways of acquiring the criteria prior to
any identification of an object with reference to them. It
is clear that becoming aware of criteria is part of the process
of learning to identify objects of certain types. And in such
cases we would not normally speak of recognizing the objects in point if we had no previous information regarding their essential properties. Frequently these properties
can be articulated in terms of other properties we have
learned to discriminate in other contexts. In other instances a novel discrimination is necessary before we can
grasp all the properties entering into the criteria for identification. The following examples illustrate this distinction.

Case (d). A regular tetrahedron may be defined in terms
already familiar to a student who has the concepts of a

solid and of an equilateral triangle. Thus in learning what characteristics are relevant to the identification of a tetrahedron, the student has no call to learn to discriminate properties with which he previously was not familiar. Learning to recognize under such conditions requires no new descriptive categories, but consists merely in learning to order familiar descriptive categories in a new way. Thus the ability to recognize objects which can be described in familiar terms can often be acquired by a merely verbal transaction without recourse to physical illustrations.

Case (e). Ability to recognize objects of a novel type sometimes can be acquired by being presented with a single object of that type, along with information concerning what the object is. A person familiar with various sorts of wine glasses, for example, might learn to recognize a brandy glass merely by being shown one and by being told what the glass is for. This information would alert someone to the fact that the configuration of the stem and base, the shape and size of the bowl, and the contour of the cross-section, all are pertinent factors in determining the identity of the object. Someone already accustomed to distinguishing these characteristics in wine glasses of other sorts very likely would be able to tell at a glance what is unique about brandy glasses.

Case (f). Learning to recognize an object whose identifying properties are different from any the learner previously had been able to discriminate involves the acquisition of novel descriptive categories. A person who could not discriminate between the sides and other features of a polygon could not be taught to recognize a 1,000-sided figure. Neither could he be taught to recognize a hexagon. At some stage in the development of a person learning to recognize increasingly difficult configurations, he must become able to focus his attention on features of these patterns which previously had always escaped his notice. Similarly, a person who did not possess the concept of an electronic element in a vacuum tube would be unable to recognize a rectifier as distinct from an amplifier without first acquiring that concept.

In Cases (d) and (e) the subject is able to learn the identifying criteria of a novel sort of object without having first to acquire the ability to distinguish characteristics of which previously he was unaware. In cases like (f), it is part of his learning to recognize a novel sort of object that he learn to distinguish novel characteristics as well.

Learning to focus attention upon novel characteristics is not simply a matter of instruction or of behavioral conditioning. A child may be presented with several objects which have only the color red in common in an effort to teach him the use of the term 'red'; but unless he has the ability to consider the color of an object apart from its shape or size, no learning will occur. A pigeon can be taught to discriminate basic colors and shapes, but only because pigeons have the ability before conditioning to concentrate upon color in some of their responses and shape in others. This ability to isolate features of his environment perhaps can be reinforced in a pigeon. But the basic ability to isolate characteristics is a necessary condition of our being able to reinforce any of his responses or to change the structure of his behavior in any predictable way. Similarly, when a person attempts to learn how to recognize an object some of whose identifying characteristics are novel to him, he can do so only if he is able to focus his attention on instances of those characteristics and to consider them as distinct from other characteristics which may be present in the object he is observing.

The ability illustrated in Case (f), which is different from anything present in Cases (d) and (e), is that of acquiring new descriptive categories, which cannot be defined or taught in terms of other categories with which the subject previously was familiar.

Let us consider now to what extent these features of human recognitive behavior can be duplicated by mechanical classification procedures based on digital computers.

4. The term 'invariant' has been used to refer to the characteristic or set of characteristics which distinguishes a given class of individuals from all other classes, and the possession of which qualifies an individual for membership in that class. As noted in the previous chapter, the problem of preparing a machine to recognize a given pattern has been conceived, almost without exception among current researchers in this area, as involving the problem of finding out what characteristics are invariant for the class of individual instances of that pattern. Three general approaches towards the mechanical recognition of letter-patterns have been discussed. The simplest of these, the method of template matching, involves providing the machine with a standard figure against which particular instances of the pattern to be recognized can be matched and tested for deviation. If the recognition system is based on a digital computer, both the standard figure and the pattern to be recognized are represented within the system by ordered series of states of bivalued elements. If the series representing the pattern to be recognized corresponds within an acceptable degree to the series representing the standard figure, the system indicates that the pattern is of the type identified by the standard figure. In such a system, this amounts to "recognition" of the pattern. The sense in which such a system can "recognize" a letter-symbol is analogous to the sense in which a slot machine can "recognize" a coin (or a slug). Because of their considerable variability, such a method holds no promise for the satisfactory recognition of handwritten letter-inscriptions.

A more promising approach is provided by the method

of listing various properties or features, some combination of which we might hope to provide an invariant capable of accommodating a wide range of different inscriptions of a given letter. Now it is clear from the outset, if our remarks in connection with Case (a) above are correct, that we cannot hope to specify in advance a set of features which can be relied upon for the identification of all inscriptions of a given letter even by penmen of undoubted competence. This method might serve well enough when applied to limited samples of letter-inscriptions written by particular penmen under particular conditions. But our concern here is with the mechanical recognition of letter-symbols written by the literate public at large. And if we cannot say in advance what features of a symbol are necessary and sufficient for its being an inscription of a certain letter, then we cannot say in advance what features might serve as invariant for the mechanical classification of that letter. The more enterprising among researchers, of course, might experiment with various combinations of features which seem to be present in properly shaped letter-symbols, hoping that some combinations will turn out to be at least partially reliable for the identification of at least some of these letters. But this approach, besides being haphazard, is costly and time-consuming. It is customary today, instead, to enlist the aid of a computer in the attempt to find suitable invariants for the mechanical classification of letter-symbols. To this end the self-optimizing capabilities of our more flexible computers have been employed with the expectation that the machine can "learn" to classify letter-symbols presented to it by trial and error. As we have seen, the programmer's part in a system of this sort is to supply the computer with a list of features in terms of which letter-patterns presented to it can be described, and to prepare an operating routine which, as "learning" proceeds, will lead the machine to bias its procedures of selection in favor of those features which result in a high percentage of correct classifications. When the "learning phase" is completed, the machine should have evolved a set of criteria which give the highest percentage of correct classifications of which it is capable.

Powerful as it may appear, this method has severe limitations which become obvious when we bear in mind the difference between Cases (d) and (f) above. Not only are humans able to recognize objects, the identifying features of which (if any) they are not able to specify, but moreover they are able to learn to identify objects with reference to novel features which cannot be defined in familiar terms. As we shall see, this capability is not shared by digital computers. The consequence is that a computer-based recognition system will be able to "learn" reliable criteria for identifying letter-symbols only if we are able to provide definitions of the characteristics entering into those criteria. If, as seems to be the case, we are unable even to say what features of a letter-symbol are relevant for its identification, we are returned to the impasse which by now should begin to seem familiar. As long as we have an inadequate conception of what is involved in the human recognition of letter-symbols, we have little reason to be optimistic about our chances of achieving a satisfactory simulation of this behavior.

It has just been claimed that digital computers are unable to evolve criteria for classification which are not definable in terms of categories with which they have been specifically provided. Let us prepare to illustrate this particular weakness of the self-optimizing system by first illustrating its peculiar strength.

Consider the case of a large city with severe traffic problems which turns to a computer for assistance in determining the optimal rates of change of its traffic lights in especially congested locations. Each traffic light is geared to the computer in a way which allows the machine complete control over the times the light shows green, yellow and red. Devices are set up in the streets between these lights to inform the computer of the rate of traffic flow in any street at any given time. The computer then is instructed to determine the combination of rates of changes of the various traffic lights, which results in the least over-all delay in traffic during times of day when traffic normally is heaviest. Since it would be fruitless for the programmers of the computer to attempt to anticipate all contingencies of traffic that the machine might encounter at various times of the day, the particular combinations of rates of changes which the computer will test must be determined by the computer itself. The machine begins by providing a fixed rate of change for all traffic lights concerned, and determines the over-all rate of traffic flow under these conditions. Then it begins to experiment by varying the rates of key traffic lights randomly and checking in detail the changes in traffic flow which result from these variations. Soon certain combinations of rates are found to result in appreciably improved traffic flow. These combinations are noted by the computer and given preference over other combinations in its further experimentation. By recording and continually re-examining the traffic conditions which result from each combination it tries, and by continually altering its processing routines to increase the probability that favorable combinations occur more frequently than unfavorable combinations, the computer soon evolves a set of normal working instructions which enables it to control traffic during peak periods in a near-optimal fashion.[3]

In this example, the computer is given the specific task

---

[3] The illustration is oversimplified, but in theory something like it is workable. A good discussion of practical problems of traffic control by computer is in "Traffic," by Evan Herbert, *International Science and Technology* (May 1964).

of achieving optimal traffic flow and is provided specific criteria for improving its performance. But it is not told specifically how to perform the task. Instead it is given instructions for altering its own operating procedures until an optimal traffic flow is achieved. This example is typical of many uses to which computer techniques of self-optimization already have been applied, both in civilian and in military contexts. Although there are still difficulties in this sort of application, they do not seem insurmountable. It is important to note in all such cases, however, that the computer must be provided with instructions for undertaking its process of adaptation, and with criteria as well for determining when optimal results of this process have been achieved. These two conditions are absent in the next example.

Conceive now of a group of speculators who engage a computer to predict stock market fluctuations. At first they attempt to provide the computer with data which would be relevant to its predictions, such as rates of change of major commodities during typical market conditions in the past, buyer activity during recent weeks, states of health of key executives, and similar matters. But the computer's results with these data are not encouraging. Finally they hit upon the idea of letting the computer select its own data on which to base its predictions. The computer is to follow its own promptings, not only in selecting the data to be considered, but also in determining what form the data is to take for processing. By giving the machine complete freedom in selecting and organizing its data, the speculators hope it will originate a set of categories for describing and processing market information which could not have been anticipated by human means alone.

To appreciate better the plight of this computer, recall that all information is processed by a computer in the form of series of electromagnetic charges. Different items of information are represented by different formations of these series. For the computer to accept a bit of information, it must be presented in a way which admits unique translation into one or another of these serial formations. Since many different items of information will be supplied to a computer in a typical problem, the person supplying the information must share with the computer a set of well-defined conventions regarding how much data in a given series of charges is relevant to a particular item of information, and regarding the order in which information of different kinds will be presented over a given period of time. These conventions are the only means the computer has of organizing the discrete electromagnetic signals presented to it in a way enabling them to be construed as representing information. Without these conventions, the input signal could represent nothing but itself; the charges could not be taken as part of an information-laden pattern.

By refraining from specifying the form in which information is to be presented to their computer, and by requiring that it impose order on its data without preliminary instructions of human origin, the speculators have assured themselves of results devoid of intelligible content. Computers at present cannot originate their own categories for information processing, and no good reason appears to anticipate that machines of the future will be more talented in this regard.[4]

The example of the traffic-control computer is parallel to Cases (d) and (e) above, in which humans learn to recognize on the basis of familiar characteristics combined in

---

[4] The method of Uhr and Vossler described briefly in the previous chapter seems to constitute an exception. If so, it is not an exception which affects the point of the discussion above. The "operators" of their system "describe" the input pattern in a very indirect way at best, and the "descriptions" are limited to spatial features.

previously unfamiliar ways. Self-optimizing programming methods are well suited for learning situations of this type. The example of the speculating computer, however, involves pattern-recognition in terms of entirely novel characteristics. Human recognizers seem to be capable of this, as illustrated in Case (f); but computers, we have argued, are not.

Let us now bring these results to bear explicitly on the question of the feasibility of simulating human letter-recognition with mechanical classification systems.[5]

5. We have been considering the suggestion that a classification system might provide the basis for an adequate simulation of human letter-recognition, even though recognition itself is not a form of classification. Several remarks relative to this suggestion are warranted by the preceding discussion. (1) Insofar as we are unable to specify the features of a given letter-symbol by virtue of which that symbol represents a particular letter and no other, we are unable to provide any classification system (mechanical or otherwise) with criteria by which it can be expected to perform an adequate classification of that symbol. If we cannot specify criteria by which we recognize letter-symbols, we cannot specify criteria by which computers might be expected to classify them.

But the possibility remains that the rather remarkable "learning" capacities of modern computing machinery might be relied upon to develop complex and unexpected characteristics with reference to which letter-patterns could be reliably classified. Although this cannot be denied as a sheer possibility, our hopes in this direction should be restrained. For it is the case (2) that computers can do

---

[5] The method of segmentation has been omitted from this review. In fact, it appears to be the most promising of the three approaches. The reasons for this, however, cannot be discussed before the final chapters of this book.

no more than combine in various ways the basic descriptive categories with which they are provided by their programmers; and insofar as we are unable to say what features of letter-patterns contribute essentially to their identification, there is no reason to hope that computers will be able to build up adequate classificatory criteria out of the categories we provide by guesswork.

In view of the fact that humans seem typically to recognize letter-symbols without reference to defining criteria, we should be aware finally of the possibility (3) that there simply *are* no necessary and sufficient features of the sort we have been seeking for the identification of the letter-symbols of our written alphabet. At least it appears likely that none of the more obvious *spatial* features of letter-symbols provide criteria of this sort. It may be the case, of course, that there are criteria of the sort we have been seeking, but that they are not to be found among the spatial or topological features of the symbols themselves. That this is in fact the case cannot be argued now, but considerable reason for believing so will arise in the discussion of Part Four of this essay.

In short, we have arrived at a conceptual impasse. We do not know how to define the letter-symbols which we wish to classify mechanically. We do not know consequently how to provide criteria for their correct classification. And we do not know how to go about improving the performance of those classification systems which have already been constructed in hopes of simulating human letter-recognition. The deficiency in point here lies not in the nature of the computer itself, nor is it a matter merely of "the state of the art." The deficiency rather lies with the fact that we do not understand the type of behavior we are attempting to simulate with our classification mechanisms.

Attempts to simulate letter-recognition with classification systems undoubtedly will continue, and various improvements may now and then appear. But the fact of the matter is that our attempts to achieve mechanical pattern recognition are without adequate conceptual foundation. Humans are capable of responding accurately and consistently to a wide variety of letter-patterns. But we simply are unable to specify features of these patterns which are essential to their being identified. As long as recognition is conceived as a matter of applying classificatory criteria to instances of the pattern to be recognized, it appears that recognition of even the simplest patterns which humans handle day in and day out without difficulty is beyond the reach of even our most sophisticated computer systems.

The theme of this book is that the way out of this conceptual impasse is not in the direction of a continued search for spatial features with reference to which letter-symbols might be classified, but rather is to achieve a better understanding of the behavior we are trying to simulate. There appears to be no better way to begin than by undertaking a detailed analysis of the concept of recognition itself.

PART II

PROCESSES

AND

ATTAINMENTS

CHAPTER FOUR

MARKS OF THE
DISTINCTION

1. Consider a gardener gazing appreciatively over his lettuce patch, when suddenly he recognizes the head and ears of a partly concealed rabbit. Just prior to the moment of recognition, let us say, he was engaged in only one visual activity—gazing with pleasure over his crop, but gazing at no one object in particular. At the moment of recognition does he begin suddenly to do two things with his eyes? Whereas before he was only gazing, is he now both gazing and recognizing? There are alternatives. We might say he has left off gazing for recognizing, and so is still engaged in only one (but a different) visual activity. Or we might say he is doing the same thing (looking), but doing it in a more sustained or attentive way. Another alternative is that the question 'How many things?' is not a proper question in this situation, or that as the question stands it does not admit a straightforward answer.

There are questions like this which are easy enough to answer. The gardener may be strolling down a path while inspecting his vegetables, in which case he certainly is engaged in at least two activities. He is strolling and looking, and he may as well be smoking, whistling and scratching his ear. If he is only smoking at one moment and then begins to whistle, we would be content to say he is engaged first in one and then in two oral activities. If he stopped rubbing his ear and picked up a clod to throw at the rabbit, he would be leaving off one manual activity for another. Or if he were to begin striding rapidly in the direction of the rabbit to frighten it off, we would say he was doing much the same thing with his feet (walking), but doing it with more determination (strolling, then striding).

If time-and-motion specialists were engaged to determine how many things the gardener does during a typical minute of gardening, the answer might be that he hoes, pulls weeds, looks for ripe vegetables and smokes, and that typically he is engaged simultaneously in more than one of these activities. It might be determined, moreover, that each of these activities is independent of the others. Pulling weeds does not require hoeing or smoking on the part of the gardener, nor does it commit him to any particular way of doing one of these when the occasion arises. He may begin or leave off looking for ripe vegetables without beginning or leaving off smoking, hoeing, or pulling weeds.

But the boundaries between gazing (or other forms of looking), on the one hand, and recognizing (or noticing or detecting), on the other, are not as clear as the boundaries between smoking, hoeing and similar activities. A person may gaze at a scene without recognizing anything, but could a person recognize something (visually) without gazing at it? At least, we probably would want to say, he must be looking at an object in *some* way in order to recognize it. But, how many different ways of looking are there?

Our concepts of looking and of recognition need clarification before we can answer questions like these. And if it should turn out that these are not questions of the right sort to ask about perceptual situations, it would become important to determine what questions are of the right sort. For these questions, or questions like them which are more properly phrased, are central to the problem of achieving satisfactory recognition mechanisms.

These questions may appear at first, indeed, to be questions for the man with leisure and a flair for riddles. In fact, they are philosophic questions. But the attempt to answer them, or to make them fit for answering, has practical ramifications. Suppose the gardener were disturbed enough by rabbits to seek assistance in guarding his crop, and sets about to build an automatic rabbit detector. No mere "garden-watcher" will do. He needs more than an apparatus to keep the garden area under surveillance, more than a camera or photoelectric cell which responds whenever anything moves in the garden. What he needs is a "rabbit-recognizer," some sort of device to distinguish between rabbits and other creatures which move about gardens when no one is looking. It may be a fairly routine matter to build a "garden-watcher" (or an air-surveillance radar, or a subterranean-shockwave monitor), but it is not within our engineering routines to construct a satisfactory device which detects rabbits alone (or only enemy aircraft, or atomic blasts but not earthquakes).

The questions about the likenesses and differences between gazing and recognizing begin to appear more significant. Gazing belongs to the same class of activities as scanning, watching, looking, viewing and listening. Detecting and recognizing are members of a class including as well perceiving, discerning, espying and discriminating. Members of the first class all have the feature of being *observational processes*. Members of the second are all *perceptual attainments*. It is important to know how the concepts of these processes and the concepts of these attainments are related. Being able to distinguish clearly between gazing at a rabbit and detecting a rabbit, for example, is not in itself to be able to build a "rabbit-recognizer." But no one can build a device to perform a specific function satisfactorily, except by luck, if he does not have an articulate and pertinent conception of the function itself.

2. There is as much difference between asking 'How long did it take you to recognize the error?' and asking 'How long was your recognition of the error?' as between sense and nonsense. Coming to recognize an error is a process which has a beginning and an ending, and hence which takes a certain amount of time. But the recognition which occurs at the end of the process has itself no start or finish. Hence it is unintelligible to inquire concerning the length of the recognition itself.

There is a parallel difference between 'How long was the battle which you won?' and 'How long was your winning?'. The process of fighting a war takes time, and is terminated if successful by victory. But the victory itself is not time-consuming. This is not to say, of course, that one can find time to win a war no matter how busy one's schedule. The point is not that victories require relatively little time, but rather that they require no time at all. And the reason victories do not require time is simply that they are not activities which have duration. Pursuing a military campaign itself is a competitive process which has an approximately datable beginning and end. But victories, being the denouements of competitive processes, do not themselves have a beginning or an ending. Thus, whereas battles typically are dated by pairs of numbers designating spans of time, a victory normally is dated only by a single number marking the termination of the struggle.

Because victories are not activities[1] which admit duration, the question 'How long was your victory?' fails to suggest any intelligible answer. For the same reason, there is no sense to be made of 'How long was your recognition of the error?'. The *companion* question 'How long did it take to recognize the error?', when asked of a logician, an architect, or an accountant, might occasion the intelligible reply 'two hours' or 'three years'. But unless he took 'How long was your recognition of the error?' as an inept way of asking this other question, none of these practitioners would be prepared to assign time limits to the success of his efforts to find his mistake.

This distinction between campaigning and winning, or between looking for an error and finding it, will be signified by the terms 'process' and 'attainment'. It is the mark of a process that it has duration. But an attainment, although datable, is not time-consuming. The questions 'When did it begin?' and 'When did it end?', when asked of any process, will admit an intelligible answer. Either question asked of an attainment, however, would fail to convey any intelligible meaning.[2]

Process and attainment words generally (not invariably) occur pairwise in our language. Thus we have 'fighting' and 'winning', 'seeking' and 'finding', 'deliberating' and 'deciding'. If a combatant is successful in fighting a battle, he wins it. If a detective's search for the culprit comes off properly, he finds his man. The attainments of winning and

---

[1] 'Activity' generally will be used as synonymous with 'process' in this essay; the term 'act' will be reserved to cover both processes and attainments.

[2] The term 'process' here corresponds closely enough to the term 'process' as used in G. Ryle's *The Concept of Mind* (New York, Barnes and Noble, Inc., 1949), pp. 135 ff. The present use of 'attainment', however, is different from that of Ryle's 'achievement'. Whereas attainments by definition have no duration, achievement terms, as Ryle puts it, might "signify more or less protracted proceedings" (p. 149). Attainments, moreover, as we shall see, are not invariably or even typically (as are achievements) the successful results of "certain acts, operations, exertions or performances" (p. 151).

finding are the successful outcomes of the processes of fighting and seeking. A physician's practice on a patient might be described by 'examination' or 'treatment', and if everything goes well by 'diagnosis' and 'cure'. A marksman shoots and hopes to score. It is a feature of each of these examples that the attainment would not occur without the process preceding. Winning a war requires fighting (else there is no war), and curing a patient requires some sort of treatment.

It would be mistaken to conclude from these examples, however, that the union between process words and attainment words in our language is unvarying. It is plain from the start, for example, that 'winning' is not monogamously wedded to 'fighting', for 'winning' might designate the outcome of a variety of activities, of which running, playing, contending and wagering are only a few examples. Detecting an error might be the successful outcome of a mathematician's routine checking and rechecking of his steps; but it might as well be the result of a laborious reconstruction of an attempted proof which previously had failed to cohere. A prisoner might gain his freedom by satisfactorily serving his term, by a successful appeal for parole, or more directly by jumping the walls. There is more than one type of process which might result successfully in the finding of a missing pen, and more than one way in which to contrive to win an election or to pass a course. Thus any suggestion that attainment words of a given type are uniquely coupled with process words of a single corresponding type must be rejected.[3]

These examples might suggest, nonetheless, that an attainment invariably is the successful outcome of a process which involves a deliberate attempt to bring about that attainment as a result. This suggestion also is to be resisted. Whereas some attainment words certainly designate suc-

[3] The relationship between attainments and their attendant processes is more fully examined in Chapter Five.

cessful outcomes of deliberate endeavors, others do not designate successes at all.[4] Yet other terms of attainment designate successes, but successes which are not the outcome of any deliberate endeavor. Illustrations of the latter type are commonplace. Experience with finding lost objects often seems to indicate that a person has almost as good a chance of finding something he wants very much when he is not looking for it as when he is conducting a deliberate search. A lost wallet might turn up when one is rummaging idly through a drawer in an old chest ("So that's why I couldn't find it: the children must have put it there last winter"). The cleaning lady as a matter of course finds lost buttons and pins while looking for nothing in particular. A halfhearted suitor might attain matrimony rather against his will, and hence, it could be said, without really trying. People win lotteries in which they did not know they were entered, and a candidate might win an election (say to the position of secretary of a social club) even though all his campaign efforts were directed towards persuading the voters that he really is not the best man for the job. Although of course the winning of elections, as well as the finding of lost items, are often results of strivings, the success in each of these particular examples does not follow any deliberate attempt to achieve the end in question.[5]

Other expressions of attainment designate happenings which normally would not be counted as successes at all.

---

[4] This is another difference between attainments, as here conceived, and Ryle's achievements (cf. *The Concept of Mind*, p. 149).

[5] One dictionary-meaning of 'success' is that of "favorable termination of a venture." Just as we might say that someone succeeded "without half trying," so might we say in this sense that someone succeeded without trying at all. A venture could be successful even though its particular outcome had never been anticipated. It seems to be the case in general, however, that the outcome of a venture is considered to be successful only if under some (perhaps different) circumstances that outcome *might* be the object of a deliberate endeavor. Since, as noted in a subsequent example, one does not *try* to reach the age of twenty-one, attaining one's majority would not normally count as a success.

Now we should not want to say that some attainments are failures. Losing a race, while nondurational in the same way as winning, does not constitute an attainment; nor does defeat in battle, failure in litigation, nor missing a bus. Examples of attainments which are not successes are not to be sought among failures, but instead among happenings which ordinarily would be considered neither failures nor successes. One example is the coming of legal age of a young citizen, described by saying he reached his majority. Now there seems to be no straightforward sense in which one might be said to *try* to reach the age of twenty-one, and accordingly there seems to be no clear sense in which reaching twenty-one counts as a success. One can succeed only in an undertaking in which, for reasons of competition or another sort of contingency, one might also conceivably fail. But as long as one remains alive, he cannot fail to reach the age of twenty-one. A person might fail to remain alive, of course, but this seems to be the only failure invariably involved in the demise of a person before his twenty-first birthday. And success in the endeavor to stay alive is no more fully realized in reaching the twenty-first birthday than in remaining alive during the day preceding or the day after. For another example of this sort, consider the event of coming into an inheritance. 'Inheriting' designates a happening in which, apart from a deliberate attempt to influence the will or to hasten the departure of the benefactor, one would not normally be said either to fail or to succeed. Yet to inherit a sum of money might be an attainment of considerable moment.

These examples should secure the point that not every attainment is the successful outcome of an endeavor, nor even a success in any sense which admits intelligible contrast with failure. So there are some attainment words which apply or fail to apply at various stages in a person's career independently of the outcome of any particular process or endeavor in which the person might previously have been engaged. It is part of the purpose of Chapter Five to examine other attainment words of importance for our purpose which share this characteristic.

3. The distinction between processes and attainments corresponds to a difference in grammatical forms normally taken by process and attainment verbs in general discourse. An indication of this grammatical difference is apparent in the oddity of the sentence 'I am finding my wallet', in contrast with the quite normal sentence 'I am looking for my wallet'. 'To find' is an attainment verb, conveying the sense of a nondurational happening. Since finding is not a process with temporal dimensions, the use of 'finding' to indicate a continuing activity, as with 'I am finding', is an improper deployment of that term. To use 'finding' in the present progressive tense to suggest a continuation of the "act of finding" is as unintelligible as its use in 'When did you stop finding your wallet?', and for the same reasons.

'To look for', on the other hand, is a process verb, and as such is used quite ordinarily in the present progressive tense. The expressions 'I am looking for', 'I began to look for' and 'I stopped looking for' have equally straightforward uses, and this is a good indication that looking, as against finding, is an activity with distinct temporal dimensions. The same distinction in use appears with other pairs of process and attainment verbs. It would be perfectly intelligible for a clerk to say 'I am checking for an error'; but the expression 'I am discovering an error', if intelligible at all, could only mean something like 'I am checking these figures, and think I will discover (or may have discovered) an error'. Another example is with 'running' and 'winning', although at first this may seem to be an exception. 'John is running' has an obvious use, since running is an activity with duration. But 'John is winning' also is a very ordinary thing to say. The phrase 'is winning' in this latter expression, however, does not indicate a continuation of something which might be called "the process of winning." The phrase 'x is winning' in this use is elliptical for 'x is in the process of a competition which by present indications it appears that x will win'. To use 'winning' as part of a present progressive verb to mean anything much different from this would be as unintelligible as its use in 'Did John stop winning a moment ago?', which surely is not an acceptable paraphrase of 'Is it true that John is no longer ahead?'.

The characteristic of not admitting a customary use in the present progressive seems to be typical of attainment verbs. But it is not typical of attainment verbs exclusively. A large class of terms which exhibit the same characteristic has been explored recently by Urmson under the title "Parenthetical Verbs." According to Urmson, a parenthetical verb is one which may occur at the beginning, middle or end of an assertion without change in meaning. We may say alternatively, for example, 'I suppose he is a capable scholar', 'He is, I suppose, a capable scholar' or 'He is a capable scholar, I suppose'. But we would not say 'I am supposing at this very moment that he is a capable scholar'.[6] Other verbs which find little or no use in the present progressive are those a typical function of which is to consummate agreements, contracts or commitments, and which accordingly have been called 'performative verbs'.[7] When someone says with due solemnity 'I prom-

---

6 Any one of the terms 'guess', 'suspect', 'admit', 'assume', 'presume' or 'concede' could replace 'suppose' in this example. The article, which lists other parenthetical verbs besides these, appears in *Mind* (October 1952), pp. 480–496.

7 The best available account of performative utterances is in *How to do things with Words*, by J. L. Austin, ed. J. O. Urmson (Oxford, Clarendon Press, 1962).

ise', his saying in the present tense constitutes his promising. He may say in the past tense 'I promised to do this yesterday', or in the future tense 'I will promise if it will reassure you'. But he would not interrupt his promising to say (descriptively) in the present progressive 'I am promising'. (One *could* perhaps imagine a character in a certain sort of comedy leaning confidentially towards the audience and projecting *sotto voce* 'I am promising now, but see how soon a promise can be broken'.) 'I beseech you to release your claim', when uttered in appropriate circumstances, constitutes a beseeching; but 'I am beseeching you' has no normal performatory function, except perhaps to add a tone of urgency to the beseeching. Other examples could be taken from among performatory utterances in the passive voice. 'Jones, you're fired' may effect the firing of Jones; but 'Jones, you're being fired' would likely as not lead Jones to ask "When?".

Another role commonly played by the '-ing' suffix with process words is in the formation of nouns from verbs. Thus we say 'Racing is his business' or 'He excels in hunting mountain lions'. Comparable formations with attainment words, however, often would seem distinctly peculiar; consider 'Winning is his business' and 'He excels in perceiving mountain lions'. Although attainment words do sometimes take an '-ing' ending in the formation of gerunds ('Who would have dreamt of her recognizing Mabel?'), and often take '-ing' in the formation of participles ('Recognizing his blunder, he blushed and sat down'), it seems to be more common to form nouns from attainment verbs by using a special ending such as '-ion' or '-ment'. Thus we speak of the attainments of detection, perception, recognition, decision, prediction, comprehension, discrimination, discernment and achievement. This in itself, of course, does not provide a distinguishing mark between process and attainment verbs, since process terms also are often used with an '-ion' or a '-ment' ending: we have the acts of construction, temptation, dissolution, development and treatment. There is, however, an interesting difference in general between attainment terms with an '-ion' or a '-ment' ending and the corresponding forms designating processes. Insofar as the terms in question are transitive, a distinction can be made in each case between an agent and an object of the action signified by the term. Thus the object of an act of detection, perception, recognition, etc., might be a blueberry bush, while the agent is a person endowed with normal capacities of sight or touch. The object and agent of an act of construction, on the other hand, might be an outbuilding and a carpenter; of an act of dissolution, a sodium salt and a chemist; or of an act of treatment, a patient and his doctor. Now both attainments and processes are actions, in the sense of being things that people (or other agents) do. The difference between the two sorts of act here is with respect to where the result of the action is manifest. To witness the results of an act of construction, one normally looks to the object of the act. The construction is to be found, not in the carpenter, but in the building which he has constructed. Similarly, the effect of the dissolution is to be sought in the sodium solution and not in the chemist, and the effects of the treatment are seen in the patient and not in the doctor. With acts signaled by nouns of attainment, however, it is just the other way around. The perception of the blueberry bush in itself has no effect upon the bush.[8] Whatever effect there may be is to be sought in the behavior or dispositions of the person who perceived. So, in general, the attainment is attributed to the agent rather than to the object. Comprehending the proof indeed makes a dif-

---

[8] It may be appropriate to point out here that the *observation* of the blueberry bush also would not normally have an effect on the bush. Yet there is an important class of process verbs which we discuss in Chapter Seven under the title 'observation verbs'. Any apparent paradox in this regard should be resolved by fn. 2 of Chapter Seven.

ference, but to the mathematician and not to the proof itself. And the difference between detecting and not detecting a trace of radioactivity in a salt normally lies with the scientist and not with the sample. Having comprehended a proof, or having detected an error, there are certain things a mathematician is able to do of which he was not capable before the comprehension or detection. In short, the effect of the attainment is with respect to certain changes in the behavior patterns or capabilities of the agent, throughout which change the object may be presumed in relevant respects to remain essentially unaltered.

The fact that the results of the acts of construction and of development lie with the object rather than with the agent appears to be connected with the fact that 'construction' may mean either the process of constructing or the result of the process (the structure) and that, similarly, 'development' may refer either to the process or to the end result (a housing development, for example). By contrast, there is no object one could rightly point to if asked to point out a perception, a recognition, a comprehension or a discernment.

4. We have to note finally an interesting thing about attainments which might be called their "all or nothing" character, and which in turn furnishes the basis for a further distinction in general between attainments and processes. Whereas we will want to say that attainments either occur or do not occur, but cannot occur incompletely or in part, it is commonplace that procedures be only partly observed and that processes be terminated short of completion.

There is no middle ground between winning a race and not winning. Even if several competitors finish on an equal basis, it is said that each wins (there is a tie) and not that each has only partly won. There is no such thing as getting only partly through the business of winning. But the competitor who finishes only part of the race has not thereby failed to run. The runner who begins but does not finish is listed among the competitors. But he is not listed among those who place; for in order even to place last in a race, the race must have been completed. No way of performing in a race qualifies one for *partial* success in gaining either the first or the last place.

Yet there are various things we say in qualification of terms of success like 'winning' and 'finding' which may at first seem to suggest that wins, discoveries and similar attainments might be more or less desirable, fortunate or opportune, and hence might be more or less complete or more or less adequate. Thus we may say 'He won handily', or 'He belatedly found the ticket which, if found a day earlier, would have won the lottery'. The terms of qualification here, however, refer not to the attainment itself but to the circumstances surrounding the attainment or the results following it. 'He won handily' does not mean that there was something different about the fact that he crossed the finish line first from what would have been the case if he had won under pressure. It means that he was not hard pressed in his run, the result of which was a win by a comfortable margin. But as far as winning goes, a win by a nose is no less a win than a win by ten lengths. ("A miss is as good as a mile," and a "non-miss-by-a-mile" is no better than a "non-miss-by-an-inch.") Similarly, the ticket found a day too late is nonetheless found. The discovery made under less than wholly desirable circumstances is no less a discovery than one made at just the right time and place by just the right person. And an election is either won or not won, regardless of the quality of the campaign or the margin of the victory. (There *is* an exception of sorts here. The close win in the presidential election of 1960 was taken to indicate less of a mandate for bold action than would have been indicated by a large margin. But in this case, the election was being taken both as a process to determine the presidency and as a process to gain the express confidence of the people on matters of national posture. The election constituted a qualified success only in regard to the latter process, not in regard to the former.)

Remarks to the same effect are in order regarding the other attainments we have been considering. The procedures for testing for radioactivity may be only partially carried through, but if detection occurs it is neither complete nor incomplete but just a detection. And the clumsy and accidental detection of a trace of radioactivity is no less a detection than a detection of the same carried off with great flair and technique. After only a partial examination of the evidence, the jury may decide against the defendant; but the decision is not partial, nor conversely is it whole, after it has been achieved. The prediction which does not carry is no less a prediction than the one accommodated by tomorrow's weather. And the legacy which leaves the recipient scarcely less a pauper than before is no less a proper inheritance for that reason alone.

The suggestion that terms of attainment ordinarily do not admit qualification with respect to degree of completion is intended to be compatible with the fact that we commonly use such expressions as 'he dimly perceived a figure by the roadside' and 'she did not fully recognize the significance of the disclaimer'. The sense in which perceptions and recognitions, if they occur, cannot be said to be more or less complete is like the sense in which a proof cannot fail to be valid. And here we must be careful. We would not want to say, perhaps, that the expression 'invalid proof' invariably is *inconsistent* in use. A sequence of locutions could occur without self-inflicted unintelligibility in which a teacher requests that the students' proofs be passed in for examination, and subsequently remarks that only one of the papers contained an invalid proof. The point of this remark would be that this particular attempt at proof was not correct in every respect. We may note, too, that the expression 'partial proof' seems not to be entirely without sense: a person may have proved one of two entailments necessary for the proof of a theorem of equivalence, and might describe his progress by saying he has "partially proved" the theorem. But there is a clear sense nonetheless in which an unsuccessful or incomplete attempt at proof yields, not an "invalid" or "incomplete proof," but no proof at all. The partial completion of a proof-procedure, albeit correct as far as it goes, is not an "incomplete proof" but rather at best an incomplete sequence of proven lemmas, corollaries or auxiliary theorems. It is this latter sense which is instructive as an analogy for what we want to say about the "all or nothing" character of attainments generally, including perception and recognition.

Let us return to the expressions 'he dimly perceived' and 'she did not fully recognize'. Now 'recognize' in the latter expression might be used as synonymous with 'comprehend', 'realize', 'grasp' or 'appreciate'. In such a use it would be an accurate paraphrase of 'she did not fully recognize the significance' to say 'she did not recognize the full significance'. With this there is no puzzle: to speak of grasping part of something is not to say anything in particular about the "nature of the grasp" itself. But there is also a use, not synonymous with 'realize', 'grasp' or 'comprehend', in which one might speak of recognizing a person, place or thing, and in which the act of recognition either occurs or does not occur, but cannot occur in part. 'I recognize that man' in a particular utterance could be either true or false, but never "partially true" (in this use 'I recognize x' clearly does not mean 'I grasp x', etc.). In short, I either do or do not recognize a particular object at a particular time. And in a similar fashion, either one does or one does not perceive an object. If one dimly perceives an object, one perceives it nonetheless; let it be said by way of explanation of the "dimness" that the information about the object gained through his perception is less full than might be expected, desired or gained under other circumstances. When someone "dimly perceives" an object, his relation to the object is not a mixture of perception and "nonperception," but rather one derivative from which he fails to reach full knowledge of the object which he "fully" perceives. An object which is dimly perceived is unclearly perceived, and hence perceived with less than normal articulation. In such a perception, one can tell less about the object than would be normal under more favorable perceptual circumstances. The thing which remains constant as we speak of cases ranging from less clear to more clear perceptions is that there is a perceiver and an object perceived in each case. In each case, in short, there is an act of perception. In no case is there room for a distinction between "partial" and "complete perceptions." The alternative to a perception occurring with full credentials as such is that no perception occur at all.

There are various stories about famous people in commonplace situations which tell about the surprise with which someone comes to realize that the person whom he had known for years as "the kindly man down the street" is in fact a man of renown of whom he had heard in other contexts. Although what one knows about a person in recognizing him as the man down the street might be less complete in some sense than what one may normally be expected to know about him, recognition of the man down the street as such is no less a case of recognition than is recognition as such of the founder of Relativity Theory or recognition as such of the President of the United States.

It is with reference to this sense that 'recognition' is listed among terms of attainment. Recognition of an object as a bird is no less a full-fledged case of recognition than is recognition of the same object as a thrush or as a robin. In any such case one either succeeds or fails with regard to the attainment of recognition; there is no middle ground.

CHAPTER FIVE

ATTAINMENTS OF PERCEPTION
AND DECISION

1. There is a rough division among attainments according to their involvement with reasoning and knowledge. For example, one cannot rightly claim to recognize an object without some knowledge of what the object is. And to make a decision is to reach the end of some process of reasoning, whether rudimentary or sophisticated. The attainments of recognizing and deciding accordingly may be called "epistemic." Other attainments, like winning a lottery, inheriting a fortune or crossing a border, are only incidentally (if at all) involved with knowing and reasoning, and hence may be called "nonepistemic."[1]

There is a further division among epistemic attainments along the lines of the following grouping: (i) deciding, deducing, concluding and predicting, and (ii) perceiving, recognizing, noticing, discerning and detecting. Although our concern is primarily with epistemic attainments of the second sort, there are characteristics of such attainments which can be highlighted in the contrast be-

---

[1] The distinction between epistemic and nonepistemic attainments has no bearing upon the question whether recognition, or similar attainments, can be mechanically simulated.

tween (i) and (ii).[2] With regard to these characteristics in particular, deciding is typical of acts under (i) and perceiving is typical of acts under (ii). We may therefore call acts under (i) and (ii) respectively "decisional attainments" and "perceptual attainments," without suggesting by this nomenclature that all acts under (i) are decisions or that all acts under (ii) are perceptions. Let us begin our comparison by noting an important similarity between members of the two groups.

Verbs of both (i) and (ii) are distinguished from non-epistemic verbs in general by their accommodation of propositional clauses as grammatical objects. The difference comes out nicely in varying uses of the verb 'to find'. We might say 'He found that his friend has hidden motives', meaning 'He came to realize . . .'. Now the term 'realize' for purposes of this comparison belongs within group (ii) above,[3] and may be fitted without grammatical discomfort to object clauses beginning with 'that'. On the other hand, we might say 'He found his ring' where we would not say 'He found that his ring'. In this latter use 'found' has a meaning somewhere between 'regain' and 'came upon', and although serving as a verb of attainment would not signify an act falling under either (i) or (ii) above. Similarly, there is no clause beginning with 'that' which would make any apparent sense when coupled as grammatical object with other verbs of nonepistemic attainment, such as 'to win', 'to deceive' or 'to inherit'. Both verbs of decisional and perceptual attainment, by contrast,

---

[2] We may note, in passing, the increasing use of computer systems in government and industry to assist or to replace human decision-makers on the level of middle management. Such use of computers poses its own technical problems, but these are different from the problems encountered in the simulation of human pattern-recognition. The present chapter may serve to reinforce our awareness of these differences, thereby offering further justification for an attempt to sharpen the contrast between (i) and (ii).

[3] Not all verbs of perceptual attainment are verbs of perception. See fn. 1 of Chapter Seven and the second paragraph of the present chapter.

typically are followed by object clauses of this sort. Thus it might be *predicted* by John's colleagues *that* he will soon be promoted, but *decided* by John's employer *that* he is too old to retain, whereupon John may *conclude that* his best move is to retire. So with other verbs of decisional attainment: some form of any one of the verbs under (i) above might sensibly complete the sentence form 'John . . . that he was due for a change'. In like fashion we say 'He noticed that the coat was missing' and 'He discerned at once that the proof was faulty'. And some form of any one of the verbs under (ii) above would provide an intelligible completion of the sentence form 'He . . . that something was missing from the room'.

An interesting difference between verbs associated with (i) and (ii) arises with the fact that those under (ii) usually admit as grammatical objects, without radical change in sense, either propositions or phrases designating things.[4] We say indifferently: 'He discerned that his proof was in error', or 'He discerned an error in his proof'; 'He recognized that the painting was a masterwork', or 'He recognized a masterwork in the painting'. However, although verbs of decisional attainment often are used with phrases

---

4 There are verbs which are *sometimes* used as verbs of perceptual attainment of which this is not usually the case. As Warnock points out, for example, one can say 'I saw a fox but did not know that it was one', while one cannot properly say 'I saw that it was raining but did not realize that it was' (in "Seeing," *Proceedings of the Aristotelian Society,* NS Vol. LV [1954–1955], 211). 'See' obviously is used differently in these two sentences, from which it follows that 'see' is not used as a verb of perceptual attainment in both sentences. Chisholm observes, similarly, that one may say consistently 'Jones saw the thief, but thought he was someone else and not the thief at all', whereas one cannot say 'Jones *saw that* the boy was running away' but that Jones did not accept the proposition that the boy was running away (in *Perceiving* [Ithaca, Cornell University Press, 1957], p. 165). Again it is obvious that 'see' is not used in the same sense in these two sentences. Our point above is merely that *when* a verb is used as a verb of perceptual attainment it may take either a propositional or a nonpropositional object without radical change of sense. As we shall see in Chapter Seven, 'see' often is used in some sense other than as a verb of perceptual attainment.

designating things as grammatical objects, their meaning in this use seems usually to differ from that in their use with propositions. The judge may *decide* three cases in the morning, and in the afternoon finally *decide that* he should enter politics, but these are different sorts of deciding. The jury *concludes* its coffee break, but this is categorically different from *concluding that* the accused is guilty. Dictionaries allow that one might *deduce* one's descent along a mountainside, but in an entirely different sense from that in which Aristotle purported to *deduce that* a Prime Mover exists. A case apparently to the contrary is in the roughly equivalent expressions 'I predict rain' and 'I predict that it will rain'. But 'rain' in the first is not so much the *name* of something (falling drops of water), as a slightly elliptical expression for 'its raining', which serves not as the designation of a thing but as a sentence-radical closely akin to a propositional function.[5] The complete generality of this distinction at any rate need not be insisted upon, for there are more striking differences to be examined between verbs of decisional and verbs of perceptual attainment.

2. Decisional attainments are expressed in judgments, and typically are preceded as a necessary condition by some more or less deliberate activity of consideration. Just as a judgment is not a verdict if it is not the outcome of a process of examining evidence, a judgment which is not preceded by a process of reasoning and inference is not a conclusion. And if a pronouncement is not the result of some procedure including the evaluation of signs and symptoms, it usually would not count as a prediction.

---

[5] One does not predict *objects,* but that such and such (perhaps with reference to particular objects) will be the case. For the term 'sentence-radical', see E. Stenius' *Wittgenstein's Tractatus* (Ithaca, Cornell University Press, 1960), p. 161. R. M. Hare, in *The Language of Morals* (Oxford, Clarendon Press, 1952), pp. 11 ff., uses 'phrastic'.

There are certain preliminaries through which one must pass, certain disciplines to which he must submit, if what he thinks or what he says is to constitute a decisional attainment. A pronouncement of future possibilities which is determined by lottery, or by sheer guess, even though it may turn out to be true, is not a prediction. An assertion of mathematical identity, although it might be formally provable, is not a deduction unless a procedure of proof has gone before it. And the announcement that such and such a course of action will be followed is not a decision, as against a mere expression of whimsy, unless it follows a more or less deliberate consideration of alternatives.

This being the case, there are particular procedures of a deliberative sort which one will undertake if he desires to reach a conclusion, and certain procedures of inference he will follow in undertaking to make a deduction. Thus acts of concluding and of deducing may be conceived generally as being the desired results of particular activities of consideration. And so it is with other acts of decisional attainment. Desiring to make a prediction, the weatherman will evaluate charts and reports according to well-established procedures which by and large do not vary from day to day or from circumstance to circumstance. And a lady who has the problem of reaching a decision between two suitors would exhibit rationality by undertaking a deliberate comparison of the alternatives open to her.

This helps us understand the respect in which one might fail to reach a decision, a conclusion, or a prediction. Now it is not the case in general that one can fail to do only what he deliberately tries to do. We would say that the disobedient child who refused to continue high school failed to graduate, even though he had in no sense tried, and a man might fail to recognize his brother in a crowd simply through being unaware of his brother's presence. With particular regard to decisional attainments, however, it seems that failure presupposes an attempt to succeed. The weatherman who one day is under no obligation to make a prediction, and plays golf instead, has not failed that day to predict, as he would be said to fail if he had scrutinized his charts and graphs all morning and left in exasperation without issuing a pronouncement about the likely state of tomorrow's weather.[6] Scrutinizing charts and graphs is what a weatherman does when trying to make a prediction, and if the procedure through which he tries does not end in success, a failure is registered for his attempt. Such is the case also with the jury which deliberates all night without reaching a decision, the mathematician who labors long and hard without achieving a proof, and the lady who gives up in despair after solemn reflection on the virtues and vices of her several suitors and leaves for Europe. Failure to reach a decision, to achieve a proof or to make a prediction does not mean necessarily that the procedures which were undertaken with these ends in mind have been incorrectly followed. There may in fact be no just decision to be made on the basis of available evidence, no proof to be discovered, and no reasonable prediction indicated in the confusion of conflicting data. Failure to reach the attainment for which a set of procedures is undertaken, however, does mean that those procedures in that case were unsuccessful. The important thing here is that there are particular procedures through which one might hope, if successful, to achieve an attainment of the decisional sort, and that a person might be said to fail to reach the attainment only if he has at-

---

[6] It should be noted carefully that the failure we are discussing here is failure to *make* a prediction, not failure to make a *correct* prediction. Success in making a prediction, as against success in predicting, does not entail making a prediction which turns out to be correct. Similar remarks are in order regarding the making of decisions and the reaching of verdicts.

tempted to reach it by entering into the appropriate procedures.

An interesting feature of perceptual attainments, on the other hand, is that by and large it is a matter of indifference whether one perceptual process or another may happen to have preceded them. As a consequence there is no set of particular procedures which in general one will undertake with the specific goal in mind of perceiving, recognizing or noticing, and the successful completion of which will result in one of these attainments. *Noticing* will serve as an example. We speak of noticing unlocked doors, flaws in format, and thrushes in the bush. Now certainly no one would notice an unlocked door unless he were looking at, feeling, leaning against, or in some other way sensibly observing the door. One cannot notice an object of which he is not aware, just as one cannot make a prediction or a deduction about a matter which he does not have in mind. But noticing that the door is unlocked does not depend upon any one or several particular ways of being sensibly aware of the door. In certain circumstances, of course, one is likely to notice the unlocked door only if his awareness of the door comes in some particular way—by leaning against it, for example, if the room is dark, or by looking at the catch if the door is at some distance. But in general, apart from particular circumstances, there are no processes or procedures of which noticing is the expected or desired outcome. There seems to be no single expression describing a mode of being aware of a door which fits more naturally than any other such expression into 'I am . . . . .ing, and with luck and diligence will notice an unlocked door'. 'The jury is deliberating, and with perseverance will reach a verdict' is a sentence for which a proper use could easily be found; but 'I am looking (glancing, watching, listening, etc.) and with care and perseverance will notice a . . .' is a speech pattern which seems inappropriate for any actual situation. Whether or not one notices an object—door, bird or blueberry bush—depends only accidentally upon how in particular one's sense faculties were engaged prior to the moment of noticing.[7]

Following this, it should not surprise us to note that the ways in which one might fail to notice are quite different than the ways in which one might fail to reach a decision, a verdict or a prediction. First, it is commonplace to speak of a person's failure to notice an object the presence of which is unknown to him and which perforce he had not attempted to notice. We might say 'It is fortunate the thief failed to notice your silver', and 'His failure to notice that my king was no longer in check cost him the game'. In the case of decisional attainments, as we have seen however, one normally would be said to fail only insofar as he had tried to succeed. Second, failure to notice some aspect of an object, subsequent to some process of awareness involving the object itself, does not necessarily indicate lack of success as far as the process itself is concerned. The watch on ship may successfully scan the horizon all day long, failing to the end to notice any unusual activity to the starboard; there may be no such activity to be noticed. Failure to reach a decision regarding competing suits for her hand, to the contrary, counts as failure of whatever procedures the lady may have followed in hopes of reaching a decision.

One might feel misgivings when these remarks are extended to other perceptual attainments such as recognizing and detecting. The very point of a police line-up, it may be objected, is that the witness recognize the culprit;

---

[7] Success in looking might come in finding, and one could scarcely find an object without noticing it. But it would be the finding and not the noticing which resulted from the care and perseverance of the search. Finding often does, while noticing does not, depend upon pursuing some particular observational activity.

and one of the responsibilities of proofreaders is that they succeed in their attempts to detect errors in grammar, spelling or format. So it might appear that if the culprit were not recognized in the line-up, or if no errors were detected in the proofing, there would be something unsuccessful about the proceedings. To the contrary, however, the business of proofing might be eminently successful even though no errors are detected; there may be no errors to detect and the successful proofing authenticates this. If there are errors to be detected, and they are not detected, the process of proofing is to some extent unsuccessful. But at the same time we want to say that failure to detect errors is not *ipso facto* failure of the proofing. This is quite different from the attempt to deduce a theorem, which itself fails if no theorem is deduced (whether or not a theorem to the desired effect is in fact deducible). In a similar fashion, it is apparent that failure to recognize the culprit does not in itself constitute failure of the police line-up. It may equally well be viewed as constituting success in eliminating several innocent suspects. Moreover, recognition of the culprit would not be uniquely the success of the line-up, but more broadly the success of the process of apprehending the culprit which began long before the line-up itself. The line-up which does not result in recognition is something like the cast of a line which does not yield a fish. The cast may be successful enough if a fish is caught, but it is not unsuccessful merely because one is not.

3. This dependency upon their antecedents of acts like concluding and predicting is matched by a comparable dependency of acts like noticing and recognizing upon their sequels. This in turn provides the basis for another important distinction between decisional and perceptual attainments. It was not part of the previous argu-

ment, of course, to deny that perceptual attainments have antecedents; all attainments, being datable, occur subsequently to some sequence of events or another in the career of the agent. It should be equally apparent that any attainment of consequence affects in some way the range of behavior of which the agent is capable subsequent to the act. What has been argued previously is that acts of decisional attainment are more intimately bound up with their particular antecedents than are perceptual attainments. It will now be argued that, although decisions and predictions and similar acts do indeed have their consequences, these consequences are more or less incidental to the occurrence of the act, whereas certain of the consequences for possible action which follow acts of perceptual attainment are necessary conditions for the very occurrence of the act itself.

It is a characteristic of procedures and processes in general that their enactment does not depend upon anything which happens subsequently to the completion of the procedure. Whether a forecaster has completed the procedures proper to making a forecast is no more dependent upon the correctness of his forecast than is the fact that a person has presented a suit in law dependent upon the success of his litigation. In general, whether a particular procedure has indeed been followed is already a settled matter by the time the procedure has been completed. It may require investigation subsequent to the enactment of the procedure itself to see whether it was completely or properly enacted, as may be in issue when a case is appealed to a higher court. But the fact that the procedure was complete and proper, or that it was not, whichever is indeed the case, is not altered by anything that might occur or anything that might be discovered subsequently to the *de facto* enactment of the procedure itself.

This characteristic is shared by the decisional attainments which occur as the successful termination of particular processes and procedures. If a mathematician successfully completes a process of deduction, then a deduction has been made; and this is a fact to which nothing which occurs in the future can contribute and from which no future occurrence can detract. Whether the deduction is important, whether the mathematician receives due credit, or whether his self-esteem is elevated by the results, all may lie with the determination of future events. But the occurrence of the deduction is entirely a matter of past history after the process of deduction has been completed. Now there are indeed certain behavior traits on the part of the agent which seem more or less regularly to follow an act of decisional attainment. The mathematician, believing he has accomplished an important deduction, might exhibit elation and increased self-confidence in his behavior with his colleagues. The man who has finally made an important decision might experience a falling away of frustration and a heightened sense of purpose. And a forecaster may well attend to his other business with less distraction after than before he has turned in his prediction for the week end. We would want to say, however, that none of these behavior traits are essential to the accomplishment of the deduction, decision, or prediction in point. That is, no contradiction appears in speaking about a mathematician who feels increasingly humble after accomplishing an important deduction, or in speaking of a person who cannot bring his resolve to the sticking point after making a decision. (Decisions, of course, can be *retracted,* but only after they have in fact been made.)

An interesting feature of acts of perceptual attainment is that in general they do not share this immunity to the influence of subsequent matters of fact. Consider the case of a mathematician who claims to have detected an error in a proof by one of his colleagues. Since acts of detection, although not time-consuming, are at least datable, let us say the detection occurred at t_0. Now for the claim to have detected the error at t_0 to be admissible, there are certain things the mathematician must be able to do immediately after t_0. He must be able to state *where* in the proof the error occurred. He must be able to describe the error, and to say generally why the formula or inference in point is erroneous. And he must at very least be able to focus his attention upon the lines in which the error is alleged to appear. The force of the 'must' here is simply this: if a person claims to have detected an error, but immediately afterwards was unable to say where the error occurs and why it is an error, we would reject his claim as being without foundation. The person who claims to detect, but is unable to say immediately thereafter what he has detected and where he detected it, has not in fact detected after all. The very occurrence of an act of detection depends upon certain capabilities which are not exercised until after the moment at which we would say the detection occurred, if it occurs at all. In a word, whether detection indeed has occurred at t_0 is not a settled matter until *after* t_0.

It is essential, moreover, that the capabilities which mark the occurrence of such a detection not be inaugurated before the moment of attainment. Thus if one were to claim to have detected an error at t_0, this claim could be countered not only by showing that no capabilities for locating and describing the error exist *after* t_0 but also by showing that such capabilities existed just *before* t_0. In the latter case, there would be reason to say detection had occurred prior to t_0; but if it occurred prior to t_0, it did not occur at t_0, for one does not detect an error afresh each time he directs his attention upon it. It is perhaps possible to detect the same error twice in one's career, at moments separated by lapse of memory and considerable lapse of time. But if a person is already able to locate and describe an error at t_o, there is no room for the claim that his detection of the error occurred at t_o.

Whether Socrates died in 399 B.C. is a matter for us to *find out* subsequently; but the fact remains, if there is such a fact, independently of what we may discover about the chronology of his life. But whether Russell detected an error in his theory of classes at a certain hour and day of the twentieth century was a matter which could be settled only after the moment of detection. This dependency of detection and other acts of perceptual attainment upon future capabilities of the agent has an analogue in the buying of real estate. Say that a prospective purchaser signs a check and receives a copy of the title in his name at t_n. The time of purchase of the property then is t_n, if indeed the property has been purchased. But a statement that the property has been purchased might be countered by events which occur after t_n; the purchase, although dated at t_n, could be disallowed subsequently by the failure of the bank to honor the check, by finding previously unknown liens upon the property, by discovering that the property, in fact, was not available for sale, and so forth. Only when all these matters are settled is the truth of the statement that the property was bought at t_n a settled matter. The date of purchase does not vary with the settling of these various contingencies, but the authenticity of the purchase hangs in balance until they are settled. So there are capabilities to be exercised after t_n, like being able to draw upon a solvent account through a check, which amount to a retroactive *determination* and not merely to a *post facto discovery* of whether indeed property has been purchased at t_n.[8] In this respect, acts of perceptual attain-

---

[8] This determination, of course, is not causal. It is rather a "logical" determination, in the sense of being a necessary condition for the occurrence of the act.

ment are like buying property; namely, their validation lies with what can be done subsequently to the act.

Consider the following "thought experiment" to illustrate the fashion in which decisional but not perceptual attainments depend upon their antecedents and in which perceptual but not decisional attainments depend upon what follows the act. Imagine that the authenticity (not merely the reliability) of a certain weather forecaster is called into question (he has been found flipping coins just prior to turning in his alleged forecasts). Another forecaster of undoubted standing is called in to act as referee. Contrast this with a case in which a group of people including both logicians and editors are looking over a manuscript of a new logic text and one of the logicians claims to have detected an error. Later on one of the nonlogicians of the group asks another logician present "Did he really detect it just *then,* or had he seen it before? He seemed to find it so quickly!" In the first case we want to know whether the forecaster "really predicted" tomorrow's weather; in the latter case we want to know whether the logician detected the error *then,* or some other time, or perhaps did not really detect an error at all. The element of suspicion is not essential to these cases; what is important is that we have an expert judging the performance of another alleged expert in his field. Now here is the contrast. Imagine that the expert forecaster observes the activity of the other man (including a flip of a coin) issuing in the utterance 'four inches of snow tomorrow', after which the other promptly leaves the room. The expert has witnessed everything pertinent to making his judgment by the time the other has left (and announces: "He's a very thorough forecaster; no available information was ignored. But the business with the coin at the end *is* eccentric"). Now imagine that the expert logician has observed everything about the behavior of his fellow (he had merely looked at the page) prior to the announcement that he had detected an error, but that the latter has left the room immediately after that announcement. Under these circumstances, the expert would be unable to say whether the other had actually detected an error. He *might* have been bluffing, and certainly was bluffing if he could not at least point out the error to others present. But he left before this could be put to the test. All of the information necessary to judge the authenticity of the prediction is available by the time the words about tomorrow's weather have been spoken; but the logician who leaves after claiming to have detected an error deprives his listeners of information essential to judging the correctness of his claim. Now turn these examples about. The expert weatherman comes upon the scene just as the weatherman under suspicion utters 'four inches of snow tomorrow'. Although he can question the other about the procedures leading up to this announcement, the possibility of dissimulation is present and pertinent. He came too late to be able to tell whether the other actually had made a prediction rather than merely an irresponsible guess. If the expert logician were to arrive just as the other logician claims to have detected an error, however, he is able to assess the correctness of this claim by observing the subsequent behavior of the other. Questions of dissimulation do not arise; if the other can point out the error, explain what is wrong, and prove that he had not previously seen the page, no interesting question remains regarding the truth of his claim. What happens *before* is essential to the act of predicting, but not to the act of detecting. And so with perceptual attainments in general; what determines the authenticity of the act is what happens after the time of occurrence of the act itself.

This feature of perceptual attainments may be illustrated finally with regard to letter-recognition, and a puzzle which appeared in Chapter Three thereby illuminated. As we have noted, there are numerous objects of a common sort which we can recognize easily and consistently, but for which we are simply unable to provide a statement of what criteria (if any) there may be by which we recognize them. Most literate persons, for example, recognize letters of their alphabet without appreciable risk of failure. Yet we have argued that few would be able to say exactly what features of a given letter make it that letter and no other. If it were otherwise, the simulation of letter-recognition would pose no serious problems of a conceptual nature. This points to the conclusion that there is no set of shape or topological characteristics of a given letter which might serve to distinguish definitively between inscriptions of that letter and other letters or marks which represent no letter at all. Thus the problem arises of specifying the characteristics on which distinctions among such inscriptions might be based, for it is commonplace that distinctions of this sort are within the repertoire of every user of a written language.

This problem appears in a new light when we think of the role subsequent capabilities play in marking out the occurrence of an act of perceptual attainment. Rather than conceiving of recognition as the result of some process of classification, which is accomplished merely by successful completion of the process, let us think of it as an act essentially coupled with the inauguration of a set of capabilities to be exercised after the act. Thus, for example, after recognizing an inscription of the letter A, I am able to construe that inscription in the context of an English word, to locate it in order relative to other inscriptions of alphabetical characters, to read it as an evaluation of a term paper, or whatever may be appropriate for this particular inscription. Before recognizing it, I could do none of these things with this particular inscription; but if I could not do one of these things, or something like one of these things, after the moment of purported recognition, I could not rightly claim to have recognized the inscription. Merely seeing, or looking at, the inscription, apart from recognizing it, is not enough in itself to enable me to do one of these things. So part of the difference at least between merely seeing but not recognizing a letter-inscription, and actually recognizing it, is the difference between the absence and the presence of these capabilities. Similarly, the difference between recognizing a letter A and recognizing a letter O may be sought in view of the different capabilities which would follow two such acts of recognition. And this seems to be where context enters into the picture. For the particular capabilities which go with recognition of a particular letter may be a function of the context in which the recognized inscription occurs. Thus, for example, the difference between an inscription of A and an inscription of O, the physical shapes of which may, in fact, be practically indistinguishable, might be that one inscription appears as part of a sequence of signs interpretable without strain in meaning as saying 'The cat is missing', while the other inscription appears in a sequence of signs interpretable most naturally as 'The cot is missing'. What is required of an inscription that it be of the letter N, for another example, may be that in its context it can be combined with the letters C and A to form part of the expression 'Can you drive?', while configurationally the same inscription might count as an R in another context where it combines with C and A to form part of the expression 'I came by car'.

Thus we may say that recognition of an inscription depends in some way upon the way it is or might be used in the circumstances of its occurrence. Whether a mark is an inscription of a given letter does not depend entirely upon the shape of the mark, but depends as well upon how that mark can function within the context in question. Recognition of the inscription as being of a certain letter implies the ability, subsequent to perceiving the letter, to construe it as part of a particular context in the fashion required within that context of any inscription of that particular letter.

The fact noted above that one is often able to recognize a mark as an inscription of a certain letter, without being able to say in advance what characteristics all instances of that letter share in common, is no longer mysterious. For an inscription is determined to be the inscription of one letter rather than another by things which happen subsequently to the act of recognition itself.

The remarks of this section have been meant to apply with respect to our recognition, detection and perception of particular objects. It has been pointed out, however, that verbs of perceptual attainment also may be coupled with propositions as grammatical objects without radical change in sense. This being the case, we would expect that expressions of the form 'I perceive (recognize, detect, notice, and so on) that . . .' would stand subject to determination of the future in some analogous way. To attempt to specify even a partial list of subsequent capabilities which would mark the truth of an assertion of this form, however, would take us further into contested ground in the analysis of knowledge than can be permitted at the present. The reason for this is that any assertion of the form 'I . . . that p', when completed by filling the blank with a verb of perceptual attainment and by specifying p, entails the assertion 'I know that p'. Thus for example the assertion 'I perceive that John is in town, but do not know that John is in town' is self-contradictory, as is the assertion 'I notice that your proof is faulty in line 9, but do not know that it is faulty', or the assertion 'I recognize that the painting is a masterwork, but do not know that it is', and so forth. Perhaps it is not out of place to say summarily that no analysis of knowledge which leaves out of account future consequences of knowing can be maintained as adequate for more than a narrow range of cases in which we could rightly claim to know. For our purposes let it be enough to note that this entailment of a claim to knowledge, by an assertion with a verb of perceptual attainment and a propositional object, is not shared in general by a comparable assertion employing a verb of decisional attainment. Thus there is no contradiction in the claim 'I decided that my best course of action was to retire, although I do not know for a fact that this is the case'.

4. We may note finally a few characteristics of some attainment verbs which have been remarked by others, but which take on added interest against the backdrop of the preceding discussion. First is the orderly behavior exhibited by verbs of decisional attainment in sentences conveying commands. Juries are instructed to reach a verdict, an indecisive child may be told to decide what he wants to do, and a student may be directed in an examination to deduce 'All heads of horses are heads of animals' from 'All horses are animals'. Perceptual attainments, on the other hand, are acts the performance of which cannot be commanded. Whereas the weatherman who fails to respond properly to the instruction 'Come up with a prediction by noon today' may have disobeyed a legitimate command, one would be justified in replying that he simply did not know how to respond (beyond merely looking) to directives like 'Detect the error on page 15' or 'Recognize the third evergreen to the left.' And the officer who orders a witness to recognize the culprit exceeds the bounds both of his authority and of good linguistic sense. We do indeed often say things like 'Notice his guilty ex-

pression', intending thereby that the person addressed direct his attention upon a particular facial appearance. But if the person reports he is unable to detect what we may desire him to see, we do not consider that he has disobeyed, but rather that for some reason he cannot comply with our apparent desire.

This difference between verbs of decisional and verbs of perceptual attainment is obviously connected with the fact that there are certain procedures associated with deciding, deducing and predicting, etc., of which the attainment itself is the successful completion. The command to decide, for example, is in effect a command to undertake the procedures which might be expected to eventuate in the desired attainment. But since there are no such procedures normally connected with perceiving, noticing or recognizing, the directive that one should perceive, notice or recognize an object normally lacks intelligibility.

It is not surprising, therefore, that there should be considerable differences among the ways in which we qualify verbs of decisional and verbs of perceptual attainment. Adverbial phrases which are commonplace qualifiers of verbs like 'to resolve', 'to predict' and 'to decide' often make strained sense or no sense at all in qualification of perceptual attainment verbs. And the qualifiers we attach to forms of 'to discry', 'to recognize' and 'to notice' often do not fit with verbs for decisional attainments. The incomplete expression 'After due consideration, he . . .' can be provided a predicate with any one of 'decided', 'resolved,' or 'determined', but not by 'discerned', 'perceived' or 'discried'. We say 'he dutifully resolved' or 'he reluctantly decided', but not 'he dutifully discerned' or 'he reluctantly recognized' (except, of course, for 'The Speaker reluctantly recognized the Senator from. . . .', which is another matter). One may determine or decide on a certain course of action precipitantly, wisely or cautiously, but to say of someone that he recognized a friend precipitantly, wisely or cautiously would be to speak inscrutably or to invite questions concerning one's meaning. On the other hand, we may say that unexpectedly (to himself), or with a start, John recognized the missing letter, but we would not say that unexpectedly (to himself), or with a start, John decided to leave the room.

This difference between verbs of decision and of perception, however, is not absolute. Counterexamples undoubtedly might be found for some of the examples above. And there are some qualifying expressions which fit verbs of either sort quite comfortably. 'He noticed enthusiastically' and 'He resolved enthusiastically'; 'Luckily he decided' and 'Luckily he recognized'; 'with anticipation he discerned the path', and 'anticipantly he determined to set his course along it'—these expressions, although perhaps not invariably of high literary quality, are perfectly sensible.

A particularly engaging and final difference between decisional and perceptual attainment verbs is what might be called, for lack of a more acceptable expression, their burden of "self-authentication." For there is a sense in which perceptions, discernments and detections are self-authenticating, whereas the rectitude of decisions, predictions and deductions is in some sense independent of their status as acts of attainment. For example, one might make a perfectly proper prediction that it will rain on New Year's, whereas in fact it turns out to be sunny all that day. But one cannot properly be said to detect an error in a proof if in fact no error is there to detect. To put the thing precisely, we might say that (1) when 'I (or you, or he) perceived that . . .p. . .' is asserted to be true, the assertion '. . .p. . .' itself is not open for denial; but (2) when 'I (or you, or he) decided that . . .p. . .' is asserted, it may well be the case that '. . .p. . .' is in some way erroneous. And the same is the case respectively with other assertions of perceptual attainment in contrast with other assertions of decisional attainment. If it is true that John perceives that the dish contains three apples, then it must be true also that the dish actually contains three apples. But though it may be true that John decided that the best buy was Consolidated Petroleum By-Products, it may indeed be false that this was the best buy. Whatever propositional expression may be filled into the latter blank of the statement format 'he . . . that . . .', that expression must count as a true statement whenever it is correct to insert in the first blank a verb like 'recognized', 'noticed', 'discerned' or 'perceived'. But, given the same general statement format, a verb like 'decided', 'resolved', 'predicted' or 'concluded' might correctly be inserted in the first blank even though the propositional expression filling the second does not have the force of a true statement.

An indication of the reason for this difference is not far afield. As we have noted, any statement in which a verb of perceptual attainment is followed by a propositional clause beginning with 'that' entails another statement with the same subject in which some form of the verb 'to know' is followed by the same propositional clause. Thus 'I notice that the New Englander is late' can be true only if 'I know that the New Englander is late' is also true. 'I decided that retirement was the best course of action', however, might be true even though the statement 'I know that retirement was the best course of action' might be admitted to be false. The reason for this particular difference is that, in general, 'O notices (perceives, recognizes, etc.) that . . .p. . .' entails 'O knows that . . .p. . .' while 'O knows that . . .p. . .' in turn entails that '. . .p. . .' is true. No sequence of entailments of this sort, on the other hand, connects a compound assertion consisting of a decisional verb and a propositional object with an independent assertion of the proposition itself which functions as object in the compound assertion.

CHAPTER SIX

RECOGNITION, CLASSIFICATION
AND IDENTIFICATION

1. Suppose we were present at an eye examination in which the patient confronts a chart containing an inscription of the letter A and responds by uttering the name of the letter. Suppose then that we were to describe these proceedings in nontechnical language.

Now it may at first seem a matter of indifference whether we say that the patient *identified* the letter, that he *recognized* it or that he *classified* it correctly. There is nothing in the situation thus far conceived which suggests that one of these descriptions is less suitable than another. At least the supposed facts are compatible with each description. We should note, however, that the facts are compatible as well with the *denial* that one or another of these descriptions is correct. The patient may be in a daze, in which case we would perhaps be inclined to say that his uttering the name of the letter was more a reflex action than a case of recognition. If the patient were delirious, we might think it improper to read anything so deliberate and responsible as an *identification* into his behavior. Or if he were a very small child, it might be claiming too much if we were to say he had *classified* the inscription. (We would say this only if he could match it up properly with other inscriptions of the same letter. Perhaps he could, but perhaps also he could not.) Here are some conceivable circumstances in which it would not be pointless to debate the propriety of applying one rather than another of the terms 'recognize', 'classify' and 'identify'.

These distinctions can be sustained in commonplace contexts. Even though I could not recognize a strange flower found among my impatiens in the back yard, I could easily identify it (point it out) for my neighbor when he arrives to inspect it. A physician might be able to classify a child's ailment as due to a virus, but not be able to recognize the ailment specifically without further tests. And a botanist upon finding a large fungus in a field might be able to identify it as being of the same type as one he saw on a previous field trip, but be unable to classify it, either because it has no name or because he had never learned or could not remember the name.

It is the purpose of this chapter to sharpen these contrasts and thereby to reach some firm distinctions among the concepts of recognition, classification and identification. These differences are entirely overlooked in most of the technical literature of pattern-recognition.[1] Little help in this direction, moreover, is afforded by the relatively few philosophers who have directed their attention

---

[1] For apparent confusions between recognition and classification, see N. S. Sutherland's paper "Stimulus Analysing Mechanisms" in *Mechanisation of Thought Processes,* II (London, Her Majesty's Stationery Office, 1959), pp. 579 ff., reprinted in *The Modeling of Mind,* eds. Kenneth Sayre and Frederick Crosson (Notre Dame, University of Notre Dame Press, 1963), and E. B. Hunt's *Concept Learning* (New York, John Wiley and Sons, 1963), p. 245. Failure to distinguish recognition and identification is illustrated in "Machine Reading of Cursive Script" by L. S. Frishkopf and L. D. Harmon, in *Information Theory,* ed. Colin Cherry (London, Butterworth and Co., Ltd., 1961), pp. 301, 311.

to recognition as distinct from other forms of perceiving and knowing.[2]

In point of fact, recognition and classification are examples respectively of attainments and processes, which as we have seen are entirely different types of behavior. 'Identification' in turn will be seen to cover two distinguishable types of activity, one of which has more in common with classification than with recognition, and the other of which, although an attainment, is quite distinct from recognition or any other attainment of a perceptual sort.

Now to overlook a distinction is not in itself a mistake which requires immediate remedy. And indeed the fact that distinctions exist among these concepts does not itself preclude use of the terms 'recognize', 'identify' and 'classify' as synonyms in some contexts. Confusion among these concepts nonetheless is not benign in contexts where distinctions exist and where precision of discourse is a matter of importance. We may come to agree, in particular, that confusion of this sort is especially detrimental to our thinking about the problems of simulating human pattern-recognition. If our thinking about these problems is guided by concepts which are so blurred as to render recognition indistinguishable from classification or identification, not only is the likelihood of success in our attempts to simulate recognition thereby diminished but, moreover, we fail even to maintain a clear conception of what would count as a successful outcome of these attempts.

2 In his paper "Recognition," J. O. Urmson claims that all recognition is identification with reference to characteristic features, which in turn is intended to mean identification according to some accepted principle of classification. This leads him to speak paradoxically of "mis-recognition," as when we claim to recognize something as of a kind, *not* following an accepted principle. See *Proceedings of the Aristotelian Society* (1955–1956), pp. 259, 268.

2. A feature of most attainment verbs is their common use with an '-ion' or '-ment' ending. Thus we speak of the attainments of decision and deduction, perception and recognition. Now the fact that 'classify' and 'identify' are ordinarily used to refer to processes may be somewhat blurred, but not altered, by the fact that they also are frequently used with an '-ion' ending. The terms 'classification' and 'identification' are like 'construction' in this regard. Even with the '-ion' ending, they are used typically to refer to processes. Let us illustrate this by tracing out the parallel between 'construction' and 'classification'.

We might speak naturally of the construction of the new library or of the new construction on Storrow Drive. Our reference in the first case would be to the building activities on the site of the projected structure, regardless of its state of completion. In the second case the term 'construction' might refer to structures already completed or nearing completion. In the first case reference is to a process, in the second to an object. In neither case does the term refer to an act of attainment. In particular, the term 'construction' does not refer to the completion of the building process (as 'apprehension' refers to the end of the process of apprehending). If one wished to determine the date of the laying of the last brick, as dates are given to the laying of corner stones, he would stand a better chance of getting the right answer if he asked 'When was construction completed?' rather than 'When was the construction of the building?'. Despite its '-ion' ending, 'construction' is normally used in reference to processes or objects, not in reference to attainments.

Similarly, when we speak, for example, of the geographic classification of incoming freshmen, or the phylogenic classification of anthropoids, we speak either of the process of classification itself or of its results. One may ask sensibly how much time is required to classify the freshmen in this way (and remark "Think of how much faster a computer could do it"), or whether the classification has been completed yet (and issue instructions "If so, repeat the process with regard to family income"). And as with the analogy of construction, if one wished to speak about the end of the process, it would be more natural to use an expression like 'completion of the classification' than merely 'classification' itself.

Classification of a group of objects is a matter either of *sorting* them according to a given set of categories, or of *devising* a set of categories by which they can be sorted (as Mendeleev ordered the elements in his periodic table). Either procedure is a process and not in itself an attainment. Although the termination of the process, like the termination of any process with a definite end in view, is in some sense an achievement, what one does when he classifies in either sense has durational characteristics quite distinct from the nonepisodic characteristics which distinguish acts of attainment. We may narrow our attention to the first sense of 'classification', for clearly this is the only sense in which classification might be confused with recognition.

Now classification in the sense of sorting has all the characteristics which mark off processes against nondurational attainments such as recognition. And there are further differences of interest between classification and recognition in particular. Consider the procedure of sorting ten dozen eggs under the categories "small," "medium" and "large" which consists, let us say, of passing each egg through the smallest of three standard circular openings that will accommodate it. Not only does this procedure involve a spread of time, so that we can sensibly ask when it began and ended and how long it took, but moreover the success of each stage in the sorting process is independent of the success of any of the later stages. An error committed during the sorting of the final dozen will not reflect upon the correctness of the results of sorting the first and second dozen. In general, the success of what happens at any given stage in the process is not affected by what happens afterwards. In the case of recognition, on the other hand, whether a person has indeed recognized an object depends in a strong sense upon what he does or can do subsequently to the time of imputed recognition.[3] It is perhaps not unduly paradoxical to say that at the moment at which recognition takes place, if at all, there is in principle inadequate information available for determining whether recognition actually has occurred. Regardless of what I think at the moment, whether I have indeed recognized an edible mushroom depends among other things upon whether I still feel that the mushroom is edible when the time comes to eat it. Perhaps the mushroom actually is edible, but if I judge otherwise, subsequently I should have to say that my previous thought of having recognized the mushroom as edible was wrong.[4]

Classification has the further property, usual with processes but absent in recognition, of being open to a sliding scale of evaluation. I may classify correctly or incorrectly, swiftly or slowly, accurately or inaccurately, or merely correctly for the most part, relatively swiftly or rather accurately. My success might be partial. Even though I classify inaccurately, ineptly or incorrectly, I do classify nonetheless. Mistakes do not necessarily preclude my finishing what I had set out to do. If three of ten dozen eggs are misclassi-

---

[3] This is discussed in Chapter Five, third section, above.

[4] Notice, on the other hand, that if I claim *not* to recognize, in a sense I cannot be wrong. To recognize that p entails knowing that p, which in turn entails believing that p. So if I do not believe that p, I do not know that p, and hence do not recognize that p. When the claim not to recognize that p expresses sincere disbelief in p, then the claim not to recognize that p cannot be false. This is explored more fully in Chapter Nine.

fied, it would not be said that I had not finished sorting them after all. My *job* may not be finished, but I *have* sorted the eggs. (I may have to sort them again; my instruction when the mistake is discovered would then be to do these *again*—not simply to *do* these.) But if I recognize an apple, or a sunspot, this is something I do neither correctly nor incorrectly, accurately nor inaccurately, swiftly nor slowly. If I do indeed recognize an object, this is something I could not have done more effectively, more thoroughly or more satisfactorily. I may *look at* the object more or less thoroughly, or *search* the files more effectively; but *recognizing* the object or *finding* the missing letter, when done, could not be or have been done more or less well. Recognition for this reason may be called "evaluation neutral."

Finally, someone might command me to classify, or sort, an object or set of objects, without misunderstanding the nature of commands. A person might properly be commanded to do something which with moderate effort and due luck it is within his means to do. A runner might be commanded to run a race; but he could be commanded sensibly to win it only if his trying to do so is likely to make the difference between winning and losing. In general, only if an attainment might reasonably be expected to follow as a matter of course upon a particular activity or procedure which a person has an option to pursue does it make sense to issue to that person a command for that attainment.

The sense in which a person can be commanded to sort eggs, but cannot be commanded to recognize a bad egg, is geared to the sense in which the person who does not begin to sort eggs subsequently thereby disobeys, but in which the person who subsequently is not able to recognize a bad egg would not thereby be said to disobey. If I recognize a bad egg and fail to sort it out, I may in this omission disobey my instructions. But if I fail to recognize a bad egg, although I have examined it carefully, there is no instruction I could sensibly be charged of having thereby disobeyed. I know what to do when instructed to look, but not when instructed, as it were, to recognize. The command 'Recognize that object under the tree', even when falling upon receptive ears, is not likely to elicit any response other than some expression of bewilderment. I know what I am expected to do when commanded to classify an object as fish or fowl, but the command to recognize an object has no fulfillment within any ordinary behavioral context.

3. It remains to trace out the lines of distinction between recognizing and identifying. The term 'identification' covers acts of two quite different types which first must be distinguished. Recognition differs clearly from identification in either sense, but for different reasons. To identify is to establish the identity of something; but what is done in establishing the identity of a thing depends upon whether the problem of identity arises with the presence or with the absence of the thing to be identified. As an example of the first, consider the problem of identifying an unknown chemical in a compound. There is no question here of finding or in any other way locating the unknown; it has not been lost or misplaced. What has to be found instead is the correct designation or description of the unknown. The identification has been accomplished when the correct designation or description has been supplied. Contrast this with the problem of identifying the thief who stole the Rembrandt. In this case the description is already formulated: "the man who broke into the Museum last night about midnight, cut the painting from its frame and carried it from the building." What is to be found (or named, or in some other way located) is the person who fits this description. Until that individual is found (or named,

etc.) the problem of identification remains. The identification is accomplished when the description is found to be uniquely applicable to a particular person.

If the location of the object to be identified is known, the task of identification may be to find a name, designation or description which fits the object. Thus it would be appropriate to announce that the chemical has been identified when a chemist has supplied a name for it. The unknown is identified when we know *what* it is. Any question that might arise about the correctness of the identification would be directed with regard to the accuracy or the completeness of the description provided by the chemist. There is no question in this case whether the object at hand is the right object. In the other example, the task of identification is to find the object which corresponds to a given description. In this case no question arises regarding the correctness or appropriateness of the description. If a mistake is made, it would be one regarding the person alleged to match the description. When the person who stole the Rembrandt has been named or located, it is appropriate to announce that the thief has been identified.

In one case the task of identification is to find a description which properly fits an object already at hand; in the other the task is to find an object which properly matches a given description. Let us accordingly designate these two types respectively as the "missing-description" and the "missing-object" types of identification. These designations are for convenience of reference, and should not be taken to imply that an identification of the first type always consists in describing an object at hand (rather than, for example, merely naming it) or that an identification of the second type always consists in finding an object which has thus far escaped apprehension (rather than, for example, matching fingerprints with those of a known criminal). An identification of either sort, as a matter of fact, might be accomplished merely by providing a name. Thus we have an identification of the missing-description sort when the name 'John Jones' is supplied in response to the question 'Who is *this?*', but an identification of the missing-object sort when the same name is given in response to the different question 'Who did *that?*'. It is even conceivable that an identification of either sort might be accomplished by issuing a description, as for example, 'The Prince Regent' in response to the question 'Who is the guest of honor?' or 'The General of the Army' in response to the question 'Who was responsible for the *coup d'etat?*'. In the first case, an object (that man at the head table), itself not in question, has been provided with a description ('The Prince Regent'); in the second, a description ('the person responsible for the coup'), itself not in question, has been matched with an object (designated by the description 'The General of the Army').

We will argue that, in general outline, the missing-description type of identification counts as a process, and that, again in general outline, the missing-object type of identification counts as an attainment. We will then attempt to show that the first type of identification, far from resembling recognition, is in many respects like classification, and that the second, although an attainment, is unlike recognition in several important respects.

It may be interesting to note in passing that the distinction between the missing-description and the missing-object types of identification is comparable in several respects to the distinction between *finding out* and merely *finding*. Contrast the case of determining the name and address of a small boy who approaches a floorwalker and announces that he is lost with the case of locating the boy lost in the department store who fits the description provided by his mother. In one case the problem is to find out who the boy is; in the other case the problem is to find the boy.

So in the first instance the task is to find a description (name and address) to match a given object, while in the second instance the task is to find an object to match a given description. Similarly, identifying the unknown in the test tube is a matter of finding out what it is, while identifying the culprit is a matter of finding the man who did the crime.

Whereas it is intelligible to ask when the chemist or the detective began to find out what they wanted to know about the unknown element or the suspect, it would not make sense ordinarily to ask when the mother or the policeman began to find the missing boy or the culprit. The floorwalker may gradually find out the name and address of the lost boy by questioning him, but seldom if ever would one have occasion to say that he gradually found a missing object. (Did Alice gradually find the Cheshire Cat as it gradually appeared in the tree?) It may take the detective ten hours working behind hot lights to find out where the suspect was during the crucial moments, but finding the culprit (distinct from looking for him) takes neither ten hours nor ten minutes. Searching for something may take as long as you please, but the finding which is the successful termination of the search is without duration. Although someone might feel quite natural in speaking about how long it took him to find some article, he would probably feel just as natural in accepting, as clarification of an elliptical expression, that it was the *search* which took the time and not the termination of the search itself. An unsuccessful search which takes ten hours would include no more time in searching than would a successful search-and-finding which could occur within the same ten hours.

Another interesting difference between finding out and finding concerns the conditions under which one might normally be said to fail in either. A detective who was not attempting to *find out* an item in the suspect's recent history would not be given demerits for not finding this out in talking with the man (perhaps he was only booking the suspect). But a detective who did not *find* a notorious criminal in a small gathering, even though he was not expressly looking for the man, might well be said to have failed to find the culprit and might receive discredit for the failure. I may walk through a field and (unaccountably) fail to find any one of twenty gold pieces scattered here and there (by a robber rushing to escape without closing the stolen moneybags), even though I was not looking for gold pieces, but I would not be said to fail to find out what unknown chemical is in a solution if I had no intention of analyzing the solution. Indeed, one may either find an object or find out something of interest "by accident." But, although one may *fail* to *find* an object in a situation such that if he were to find it the finding would be accidental, one would not normally be said to fail to *find out* something if he had not intended in the first place to find something out.

In all of these respects, the problems of the missing-description type of identification are problems of finding out, and the problems of the missing-object type of identification are problems merely of finding.[5] The question 'When did you begin to identify the unknown?', put to a chemist, is equivalent to asking when he began his analysis, but the question 'When did you begin to identify the culprit?', put to a Mountie who has just apprehended his man, is pointless. The Mountie *did* identify the culprit (we assume), but what he did in doing this is not something done with a beginning, or end, in time. Identifying the unknown may be a gradual process. But identifying the lost

---

[5] Not all cases of finding out, of course, are cases of missing-description identification (one may find out how to do something, or find out who did the crime), nor are all cases of finding cases of missing-object identification (to find a missing collar button is not necessarily to identify it). So the parallelism is not complete.

boy, in the sense of finding the person who fits the description, is neither gradual nor precipitant: nor does it take a specifiable period of time, although the process leading up to the discovery of a missing person may be either brief or lengthy. Finally, one may fail to identify some heretofore missing person or thing which he is not at the moment expressly attempting to identify, as the detective may fail to identify the notorious criminal with him in the taxicab, or the doctor may fail to identify signs of cancer. But not to identify a compound in the laboratory, in the sense of not describing it, scarcely counts as a failure chargeable to the chemist walking through the room with no concern for the test tube on the counter.

4. It has been shown that the missing-description type and the missing-object type are different types of identification, and that the first is like a process in many respects while the second is like an attainment. We turn now to discuss various points of similarity between identification of the missing-description type and classification. In identification of this type the trick is to match an object at hand with a description, as against matching a description at hand with an unapprehended object. Identification of this type thus bears an obvious affinity to classification, for the problem of classification is one of arranging given objects under a set of descriptive categories.

Like processes generally, both classification (sorting) and identification (missing-description) are activities which a person can be instructed or commanded to undertake. Just as the egg candler may sensibly be instructed to sort the good from the bad eggs, so may the detective be ordered to identify a suspect or the floorwalker ordered to identify a lost child. There is one sort of subsequent behavior in either case which would count as obedience to the command and another which would count as disobedience.

Like classification again, identification in this sense is something which can go well or poorly in stages. The egg candler might sort the first dozen quite correctly, but err in the second dozen without influencing the correctness of his previous performance; similarly, the floorwalker might correctly find out the lost boy's name but fail to find out his address. In the one case we would say that the poultryman indeed has candled the eggs, but that he has not candled them correctly all in all. And in the other case we would say that the floorwalker has identified the child up to a point, or partially, but that the identification has not been completed. Thus it would seem that both classification and identification admit a sliding scale of evaluation, after the fashion discussed above, and hence have yet another feature in common.

But there are dissimilarities as well between classification and this sort of identification which must not be overlooked. Even though the eggs are candled carelessly, with poor results in terms of the final sorting, we would say nonetheless that the eggs *have* been sorted. They just were not sorted properly. But if the floorwalker or the detective were to find out little about his subject, or if what he purported to find out was inaccurate, we would hesitate to say that the subject has been identified. A poor performance in the process of identification results in no identification at all. On the other hand, identification in this respect is not like an attainment; for an attainment, if it occurs at all, occurs in a way which is not open to evaluation in terms of degrees of completion. Even though a detective could perform his grilling task so ineffectively that he completely fails to identify a suspect, one performance which would indeed count as an identification might be notably more or less complete than another performance which also results in an identification. In one case perhaps merely the name of the suspect has been obtained, while the other might produce not only his name but his address, his birthday, and a confession of past crimes as well. Perhaps we might say that the "cut-off point" (which it would be fruitless to attempt to specify apart from a particular case) between poor performance and no performance at all is higher on the "scale of degrees of completion" for identification procedures than on the corresponding "scale" for sorting procedures.

Another difference between the particular examples of classifying and of identifying (missing-description) which we have just been discussing is with regard to generality of description. The problems of identifying a lost child or an apprehended suspect are problems of finding a unique characterization of the person. If the detective's characterization of the suspect mentions only attributes which in the pertinent combination could attach to other persons as well, the suspect has not been *identified*. And if the child is described only as Bobby, and not (as he may be in fact) Bobby Jones who lives on Elm Street, he has not been identified. Yet the categories involved in classification of eggs by size or freshness, or in classification of freshmen by family income, are categories which, if they are to be applicable in such a sorting task, must be attributable with equal propriety to many individuals. It is worth noting, however, that this is not so much a difference between identifying and classifying in general, as a difference between two sorts of classifying or between two sorts of identifying in the sense of fitting descriptions to objects at hand. In the example of identifying the unknown in the chemical compound, the categories of identification are surely ones which attach to any number of individual chemical congregations. And there is apparently no inherent reason why assigning an individual thing to one of several alternate classes should not be called "classification" even though the class to which it is assigned has, or even *could* have, no other members. When Aristotle grouped all movers according to whether or not they were moved by another, the provision that the description "unmoved mover" can attach to only one individual does not seem to preclude our saying that the distinction between moved and unmoved movers is a principle of classification.

Although there is no point for the present study in any attempt to probe more thoroughly the relation between classifying and this type of identifying, it would appear that the similarities between these two procedures are considerably more prominent than any difference we have examined. It is clear, at any rate, that identification in this sense is as different from recognition as a process is different generally from an attainment.

5. It remains to be shown that identification in the other sense (that of finding an object to fit a given description), although an attainment, is not of the same sort as the attainment of recognition. Let us note some similarities first. Both identification in this sense and recognition are nondurational, and succeed or fail only insofar as they occur or do not occur at all. Neither is associated in any essential way with one specific process rather than another. For just as there are various modes of observation which could issue in recognition, so are there many circumstances of search or happenstance which could issue in the identification of a previously missing person. There is a sense, moreover, in which neither is subject to command. If someone were to order me to recognize an object (which I may or may not see), and I were (mistakenly) to take this seriously, but in fact did not succeed in recognizing the object, I could not be said to have disobeyed. Similarly, if a mounted policeman were ordered to bring back his man, and tried valiantly and persistently and intelligently to do so, but did not succeed, then his failure would not normally

count as disobedience. But differences here begin to arise. In the Mountie's case, there are certain things in general which he must do and do well in order to escape the charge of disobedience should he fail his mission. He must at least have tried intelligently and persistently. But there seems to be no procedure or way of doing things which I would have to pursue, if I were "ordered" to recognize an object, to secure immunity from charges of having disobeyed the "order." Upon receiving such an "order," as it were, I might feel motivated to look in a certain direction or to squint for a moment or two merely to avoid giving offense. But there seems to be nothing about the manner in which I look or fail to look that makes the difference between obedience and disobedience meaningful in this case. The case is rather that the notions of command and obedience simply do not apply with regard to recognition, while they apply well enough, although not without restriction, with regard at least to some standard identification situations.

There is, in fact, no specific process which suggests itself when one thinks of necessary or contributing conditions of recognition. One must be looking, gazing, perusing or listening, and at least one must be *heeding*,[6] in order to achieve recognition. But no one of these seems to be a better way of attaining recognition than another. To attain identification of a missing person, or of a culprit at large, however, there are very specific things one is well advised to do. That is why, of course, one might well be charged with disobedience if one is given a task calling for these procedures and fails to follow through.

Finally, there is a specific and significant characteristic

---

6 The term 'heeding', as used by G. Ryle in *The Concept of Mind* (New York, Barnes and Noble, Inc., 1949), pp. 135 ff., is roughly equivalent to the expression 'attending to'. One must at least be attending to an object in order to recognize it; but 'attending to' is not the name or description of a particular process or procedure.

shared by what we have called "perceptual attainments," including recognition, which does not attach at all to instances of identification. We speak both of perceiving an object and of perceiving *that* something is the case, and the sense of the term 'perceive' does not differ radically from one use to the other. Similarly, without equivocation, I may speak of recognizing John and of recognizing *that* this is John. But the term 'identify' does not even admit a propositional object.

It is clear that the relationship between recognition and classification, on the one hand, and that between recognition and identification on the other, is in neither case the relation of identity. It may be the case that *when* one recognizes, then indeed by that token one is able both to classify and to identify the object one recognizes. But to classify an object is not thereby to recognize it, nor is recognition merely a matter of identification. Any attempt to conceive of these acts in a way which blurs the distinctions among them is a theoretical mistake which, as we shall see in Chapter Ten, may be reflected in confusion of a sort which has very practical consequences.

PART III

PERCEPTUAL

ACTS

CHAPTER SEVEN

PERCEIVING
AND LOOKING

1. Consider situations which might fit these bits of conversation. (i) "I *am* listening carefully. But I don't hear a thing." (ii) "What do you discern?" "Oh, nothing. I'm just enjoying the view." (iii) "He glanced in our direction, but I doubt if he noticed." (iv) "Watch carefully, and report to me the moment you detect anything." It appears from these remarks (none of which is inconsistent) that listening does not entail hearing, that viewing does not entail discerning, that glancing does not entail noticing and that watching does not entail detecting. Similar remarks might convince us moreover that no one of the terms 'glance', 'view' or 'watch' entails any one of the terms 'notice', 'discern' or 'detect'. But here lies an important contrast. For it does not appear that one could notice, discern or detect something without at the same time glancing, viewing, watching or in some other way exercising his visual sensibilities. The contrast between these two sets of verbs will stand further examination, and for this purpose it will be convenient to have terminology for referring to them separately.

The terms 'detect', 'notice' and 'discern' are of a sort

with 'descry', 'perceive', 'recognize', and others which in
Chapter Five were called "verbs of perceptual attainment."
Let us now refer to these particular terms simply as
"perception verbs."[1] 'Perception' thus will be used only in
reference to acts of attainment, leaving the adjective 'perceptual' free to refer more generally to all acts, attainments
or processes, which may be involved in acts of perception.

We have yet to categorize 'glance', 'view' and 'watch' in
uses which distinguish them from verbs of perception.
Now there are a number of ways in which one might
glance, watch or listen without necessarily at the same
time perceiving any particular object. Let us list some of
the terms which refer to these ways under the title "observation verbs": 'scan', 'glance', 'watch', 'look', 'view',
'handle', 'hearken' and 'listen'.[2] The lesson of the bits of
conversation above now may be generalized: whereas one
might in some way observe without in any way perceiving
an object, it does not seem to be the case normally that one
can in any way perceive without in some way observing.
Yet it was argued in Chapter Five that, whereas deciding

---

[1] Note that verbs of perceptual attainment as such have not been re-
named. Although any perception verb is a verb of perceptual attainment, some of the latter (such as 'realize') would not count as perception
verbs. Note also that not every possible use of these terms would count
as use of a perception verb (for example, 'recognize' in 'If you consider it
more calmly you will recognize the injustice').

[2] In the present context 'observation' is used merely to refer groupwise
to the several acts corresponding to the verbs listed above. Notice that
'observe' itself is not invariably used as an observation verb. Sometimes it
is used this way, as in 'He must have observed the move, but he failed to
see its significance'. But sometimes it is used to refer to an attainment,
as in 'He observed that his king was in check'. Thus Ryle is able to use
'observation' to cover both protracted undertakings and their successful
completions. (See *The Concept of Mind* [New York, Barnes and Noble,
Inc., 1949], p. 222.) The fact that 'observe' is not always an observation term
may appear less disturbing in light of the fact that 'attainment' is not
always used as an attainment verb ('Attaining the confidence of his peers
was for him a most gradual process') and the fact that 'perform' itself is
scarcely ever used as a performative verb. By contrast, 'perceive' is quite
consistently used as a perception verb, at least in epistemological discussions.

normally is the successful outcome of some particular process of deliberation, there is no particular process of observation which if successful eventuates in an act of perception. This poses the problem of the present chapter. Although acts of perception obviously are in some way dependent upon acts of observation, the details of this relationship are unlike anything we have yet had occasion to examine. Our attempt to specify the relationship between observing and perceiving in turn leads to the analysis of sensation in the following chapter, and sets the stage finally for exploring the relationship between recognition and perception themselves as particular acts of attainment. Thus the Platonic division of attainments into their "natural kinds" begun in Chapter Four terminates in Chapter Nine with an analysis of the act of recognition itself.

2. Whereas perception verbs designate perceptual attainments, it should be remarked that observation verbs designate perceptual processes and thereby exhibit consistently the various characteristics examined above with regard to other process verbs like 'running', 'fighting' and 'constructing'. First, scannings, glancings and viewings not only are datable, but also have temporal dimensions. The question 'How long did you spend doing this?' makes sense when asked of the activity designated by any of the observation verbs listed above. By contrast, although the happenings designated by perception verbs are datable, they have no duration. As a consequence, perception verbs seldom if ever admit use in the present progressive tense. 'How long did you spend recognizing the bird?' (as against 'How long did it take you to recognize . . .') is senseless, but 'How long did you spend watching the bird?' is quite intelligible.

Second, there are few expressions in English which are naturally suited for reference specifically to the completion of observational activities. Such activities of course are subject to termination. We stop looking, watching and listening, as often as we begin. But in order to refer directly to the termination of these processes we usually must rely upon untoward circumlocutions like 'When I stopped watching' or 'The moment I quit listening'. A familiar form in English for reference to attainments is through use of suffixes like 'ion' and 'ment'. Thus we have 'perception', 'discrimination' and 'apprehension' to designate various acts of perceptual attainment. But no comparable forms ("watchments" or "lookions") are sanctioned for reference to the accomplishments of the processes of watching and looking.

Third, observation verbs, unlike perception verbs, do not receive propositional phrases as objects. Expressions beginning 'I recognize (perceive, descry, notice, etc.) that . . .' are routine in ordinary discourse, but the sequence of words 'I watched that . . .', regardless of how it is completed by a propositional phrase, fails to add up to an intelligible sentence, and there is no improvement when 'watched' is replaced by another of the observation verbs listed above.

These points of comparison serve to distinguish observation verbs from attainment verbs generally, and hence from both verbs of perceptual attainment and verbs of decisional attainment as these were discussed in Chapter Five. There are other respects, however, in which observation verbs are markedly more similar to decision than to perception verbs. One such feature is the propriety, in some rather ordinary circumstances, of ordering someone to undertake an observational activity. A person might be commanded to watch for hostile aircraft, to look straight ahead, or to listen carefully to the words of his superior. These are intelligible commands, and if a person fails to comply he has disobeyed where (we may assume) it was within his range of choice to obey. But one is not subject, on the other hand, to commands to notice or to discern. Failure to perceive a hostile aircraft, to detect a rattler in the path ahead, or to recognize the drift of his instructor's comments, while they might indicate incompetence or ineptness, would not normally count as lapses in obedience. A closely related point is that acts of perception, in distinction from activities of observation, are undertaken neither voluntarily nor involuntarily. There are some things one cannot be commanded to do even though one might do them willingly: win the sweepstakes, go through a period of maturation, escape injury. But acts of perception are not of this sort. One can neither be commanded to recognize, perceive or to detect, nor when one does these things can one do them in accordance with or contrary to one's will.

The distinction between observation and perception verbs is reflected in the various ways in which we qualify them in ordinary discourse. Perceptions, recognitions and detections occur with luck, suddenly or unexpectedly, but not deliberately, resolutely or compliantly. I might say that suddenly I had been able to discern the difference between Richard's and Russell's paradoxes, but would not normally say that suddenly I had been able to watch an oak tree or to handle a teacup. The things we do in observing objects and situations are things we do carefully or heedlessly, deliberately or hastily, dutifully, cautiously, or impetuously, voluntarily or under protest, sluggishly or with verve. These are ways in which processes are undertaken. But since perceptions are not processes but attainments, we would not know what to make of a claim to have perceived, recognized, or detected in a fashion characterized in one of these ways.

The fact that normally we would not speak of recognizing or detecting an object voluntarily, or with care, does not indicate that we have no control over what we do in recognizing or detecting. The point in denying that we might detect voluntarily is not to assert that whenever we detect an object we do so under compulsion. To speak of being forced to detect a faint odor or a blurred fingerprint, like being commanded to do one of these things, is as improper as speaking of detecting something voluntarily. Both the adverbs 'voluntarily' and 'necessarily' fail to attach to verbs of perception. Whatever reason might be provided for this, it presumably would be related to the fact that more is needed for the detection of, for example, the odor of mustard gas than properly functioning senses, normal conditions of observation and good intentions. One needs in addition an attentive level of consciousness and some previous knowledge of how mustard gas smells. These are abilities the exercise of which cannot be applied or withheld voluntarily. By contrast, a person with normally functioning senses, a command over his actions and proper conditions of observation can, with reference to these capacities, be said to refrain from glancing or handling an object. He need only shut his eyes or restrain his hand. I may willingly taste or willfully refuse to taste an apple; but once I have tasted it, whether I detect its sourness is a matter having nothing to do with further exercise of my will.

Clarity and candor at this point require that the notion of sensation no longer be excluded from the discussion. To observe is more than merely to exercise one's faculties of sensation. Yet there has been a tendency among philosophers of perception to minimize or entirely to overlook the difference between observation and sensation. Preliminary to a more extended treatment of this difference in the following chapter, it may be noted at this point that sensation shares with perception the characteristic of being "beyond the province of the will." In this respect at least it stands in contrast with observation. If my senses are in working order, and if I am awake and conscious, I sense. Although I may refuse to touch the stolen gem, I cannot refuse to exercise my faculty of tactual sensation. I voluntarily refuse to glance at the welder's arc, for another example, but have no immediate control over the after-images or spots of color that float in my field of vision when my eyelids are closed. Exercising one's visual sense certainly is not in itself to perceive a material object, but neither is it to view, glance, or scrutinize. These remarks do not constitute an adequate clarification of the notion of sensation, but they do provide an opportunity for explaining some omissions from our list of observation verbs which at first glance might have been puzzling.

3. It might seem strange to some readers that the verb 'to see' was not represented in the list of observation verbs above.[3] We listed 'glance', 'watch', 'look' and 'scan', but not 'see'. Similarly, we listed 'handle' and 'listen', but neither 'feel' nor 'hear'. Moreover, neither 'taste' nor 'smell' nor any roughly synonymous term was included. The reason for the omission of 'taste' and 'smell' is that, whereas they clearly have uses that fall under the category of observation verbs, they have common uses as well which would warrant their classification as verbs of sensation. A technician might speak of smelling the acid, which is to speak of observing it; but he might speak with equal propriety of still smelling a sharp odor after leaving the laboratory, and this sort of smelling, which is not to observe an independent object of any sort, seems to fit more comfortably under the classification of sensation. Again, when tasting an apple, one is, as it were, holding it under observation. But when enduring the "dark brown taste"

---

[3] It may seem even stranger to other readers that 'see' was not listed under "perception verbs." Readers of both sorts should read on.

characteristic (some say) of excessive smoking the night before, one is not observing an independent object; yet he is tasting, which is to say merely that he is exercising his power of gustatory sensation. Clearly there is a relationship between tasting in the sense of observing and tasting in the sense of sensing, but it is not one of identity.[4]

'See', 'hear' and 'feel' may also be added to the list of observation verbs, but caution is even more important here than with 'taste' and 'smell'. Whereas the latter terms seem to admit uses only within the categories of observation and sensation verbs, 'see', 'hear' and 'feel' have uses within these categories and within the category of perception verbs as well. Although 'see' is sometimes treated (mistakenly) in discussions of perception as a term of perception alone, it is more customary today to treat it as having uses both as a sensation and as a perception verb.[5] In fact, not only 'see', but 'hear' and 'feel' also, have uses under the category of observation as well.[6] Let us consider in order some uses of these terms (a) as verbs of perception, (b) as verbs of observation and (c) as verbs of sensation.

(a) 'Saw', in the sentence 'He saw the vapor trail high in the sky', is equivalent for our purposes to 'perceived' or

---

[4] The distinction between observing and sensing, of course, is not *merely* that capabilities of observation but not capabilities of sensation are exercised with reference to an independent object of some sort. The relationship between sensing and observing is examined more fully in the following chapter.

[5] One of the more recent instances of treating 'see' as a perception verb only is in Ryle's *Concept of Mind,* where the author while seeking a term to signify both discovery and search of a perceptual sort rejects 'see', 'hear', 'taste' and 'smell' which "are too narrow since they cover only achievements" (p. 233). Earlier examples of this mistake can be found in Berkeley and Hume. A. J. Ayer is less wide of the mark in *The Foundations of Empirical Knowledge* (London, Macmillan & Co., Ltd., 1940), p. 23, where he insists that 'see' be allowed to have two distinct uses, corresponding to what we have called "verbs of perception" and "verbs of sensation."

[6] W. H. F. Barnes distinguishes uses of 'feel' fitting under each of the three categories we are about to consider, in "Talking about Sensations," *Proceedings of the Aristotelian Society,* NS Vol. LIV (1953–1954), 262 ff.

'descried'. We may say 'I see that the tide is out', 'He failed to see the flagpole at the corner', and 'I can't see what Jones is pointing at'. As we would normally take these expressions, the seeings to which they refer are attainments, datable but without duration, achieved perhaps unexpectedly or with luck, but not deliberately or heedlessly. In analogous expressions, we might say 'Suddenly I heard the approaching aircraft' and 'Then I felt a sharp object against my back', or 'I heard that the motor had started' and 'Jones suddenly felt that his safety belt had snapped'. The objects of 'hear' and 'feel' in these latter two examples, of course, are of a different sort from the objects in the former, but each example here exemplifies use of a *perception* verb.

(b) Uses of 'see' as an *observation* verb are perhaps a bit more difficult to find, but nonetheless are there for the taking in ordinary conversation.[7] In asking Jones whether he has *yet seen* the airplane, we might well be inquiring whether he had yet detected it. But in asking whether he *still sees* the airplane, we are not asking whether he is still detecting it (this would be nonsensical, or at best queer), but instead whether he is still observing or watching it. Seeing an airplane in this latter sense is something one can do over a period of time. This is the sense in which we see an eclipse, and in which a lady sees her visitor approaching the door. And in a sense akin to this, an octogenarian might be said to have seen many changing scenes in his day. Unlike perceiving, seeing of this sort does not focus in a moment of attainment which can be precisely dated by a single clockreading. Analogous uses for 'hear' and 'feel' are available: 'How long did you hear the buzzing before the explosion?', 'I can still hear the watch', 'Did

---

[7] Part of F. N. Sibley's article "Seeking, Scrutinizing and Seeing" is occupied with a discussion of what he calls the "non-achievement use of 'see'," *Mind* (1955), p. 472.

you actually feel the serum flowing into your arm?', and 'She sat in frozen silence as she felt the insect crawling up her back'.

(c) Although 'see', 'feel' and 'hear' have well-established uses as perception and observation verbs, they lend themselves more readily than other verbs on the lists above to speaking about the deliverances of our various sense faculties. Without presuming complete clarity in the concept of sensation, we have noted already that, whereas one might *observe* dutifully or grudgingly, it would be senseless to speak of *sensing* grudgingly, deliberately, willingly or the like. This mark of sense-locutions is enough to enable us to distinguish between 'He felt a sharp twinge' (apprehensively, perhaps, but not grudgingly or deliberately) and 'He felt the fine texture of his competitor's velvet' (grudgingly or deliberately). Similar in this respect to feeling twinges, unlocalized aches and pains, is the hearing of vague noises, buzzes and hums which do not seem to be part of our ordinary perception or observation of material things. As noted above, we do indeed speak of hearing material things (bluejays and airplanes) and physical occurrences (explosions). But the term 'hearing' seems to fit more naturally into contexts where we are speaking of our sensations than do other verbs of audition such as 'hearkening' and 'listening'. It would be less peculiar, for example, to reply 'buzzings' to the question 'What do you hear?' than to the question 'What are you listening to?'. And if someone were to consult a physician about his frequent experiencing of unaccountable noises, he would more likely be asked 'How often do you hear these noises?' than 'Do you listen to them often?'.

It is perhaps because we are so dependent upon sight (whenever available) for our perceptual knowledge of the material world that we tend to overlook the constant flow of visual deliverances which have nothing directly to do with either perception or observation of material things. Sometimes under relatively unusual conditions our attention is forced upon such presentations. A person "sees stars" when his head is struck, sees afterimages when he closes his eyes in bright surroundings or sees apparitions of strange creatures when hallucinated. But visual sensings very much of the same character are available in entirely normal perceptual situations as well. Those who wear glasses are beset constantly with reflective and refractive images from their lenses, which they learn to ignore but which may be seen in a rich variety of shapes and colors if attended to. (Although one *learns* to suppress these images, one does not suppress them *at will*.) A recent article in the *Scientific American* explained in detail a theory of the origin of the minute flecks and concatenated rings which may be seen when one is in bright sunlight with eyes focused upon no object in particular. In a person's field of vision under quite normal circumstances there may be present shadows and shades which are not shadows or shades of anything in particular, and colors which, although perhaps associated with some object, are not color properties of any material thing. Our mode of awareness of these appearances does not constitute an attainment, and we do not normally have occasion to observe them, but surely there is a sense in which we *see* them. This sort of seeing illustrates visual sensation, a topic due for more sustained discussion in the following chapter.

4. With these distinctions among perceiving, observing and sensing in the background, it is time now to turn to the problem of tracing the relationship between particular occurrences of perception and observation. It is apparent that there *is* a relationship, at least in some cases, since the situation in which we normally perceive or recognize an object is one in which we are also watching,

viewing, handling or in some other observational fashion attending to the object. At the same time, it is an ordinary thing, as we have seen, to be engaged in observation without at the same time perceiving, detecting or recognizing a particular object. One can hearken to a sound in the distance, but not recognize it (or its source). The watch on a warship may scan the horizon, hoping they do not perceive what they are looking for. When a person views an entirely new scene, or a poorly illuminated movie projection, he may perceive nothing in particular. And one may see, in the sense of 'glance at', yet fail to see in the sense of 'perceive'. The relationship between observing and perceiving thus appears closely analogous to the relationship between racing (a process) and winning (an attainment), for clearly one can race without winning but cannot win without racing.

In line with this analogy, it seems plausible at first to hypothesize a more specific relationship between a given perceptual attainment and the observational process which accompanies it than merely the conditionality of the first upon the second. Running a race is a process which necessarily has a termination, for it makes no sense to speak of the winner continuing to run the race after the race is won. That is to say, the attainment of winning the race is the *same thing* as the termination of the process of running the race for the winner. Similarly it may be agreed that the attainment of reaching the peak is identical with the termination of the process of climbing the mountain. As Ryle puts it, "When a person is described as having fought and won, or as having journeyed and arrived, he is not being said to have done two things, but to have done one thing with a certain upshot."[8] Arguing on the crest of this analogy, he concludes that achievements (including perceptual attainments in our categorization) "are not

---

8 See Ryle, *The Concept of Mind*, p. 150.

acts, exertions, operations or performances, but, with reservations for purely lucky achievements, the fact that certain acts, operations, exertions or performances have had certain results."[9] Following the analogy of racing and winning, let us formulate the following conjecture for testing.

(C1) Attainments signified by perception verbs are (identical with) successful denouements of striving processes signified by observation verbs.

It need not be part of this to claim that all successful outcomes of observational processes are acts signified by perception verbs. Room must be left for attributing success to the endeavors of the seaman who gazes into the night for his allotted time without perceiving so much as a flicker of light. The claim of C1 rather is that attainments of perception when they occur are nothing more nor less than successful outcomes of observational strivings. This appears at least to be a reasonable interpretation of what Ryle has said about perceptual processes and achievements, and at any rate is worth examining on its own merits.

Now some of the objections which we must raise against this conjecture stem from characteristics of perceptual attainments which have been discussed in Chapter Five. The difficulties center around the fact that, with the exception of a few verbs like 'look (for)', 'watch (for)' and 'scan', verbs of observation simply do not stand for processes of endeavor. In the first place, glancing, viewing, handling and listening are not activities in the pursuit of which one need be *attempting* to do anything at all. In some cases of glancing or viewing, for example, there is no question of success or failure with reference to which it makes any sense to evaluate the outcome of the process. One might simply glance upward, idly and with no thought for what

---

[9] *Ibid.*, p. 151.

one is doing; or one might pause to enjoy the fragrances of the air after rain, innocent of any purpose to be accomplished. In the second place, even when activities of observation are undertaken with some definite end in view, and hence in some way constitute strivings, the success of these undertakings need not be contingent upon any particular outcome of the activity. In glancing to the rear, or in viewing the sunset, we might have some definite purpose to fulfill, but might not be trying to do something that is not already being done with the very undertaking of that activity apart from any perception that might arise in or at the end of the process. There are frequently cases in which once we have begun to glance, view or hearken, we have already experienced as much success in that activity as is in the offing. Although it may be that on occasion success of the activity of looking (for trespassers) comes with detecting what one is looking for, it simply is not the case in general that perceptual attainments are the successful terminations of observational processes which theretofore remain unfulfilled. Even in cases where perceptual attainments stand at the end of observational processes, it is not necessary that these attainments constitute the success of the observation. Although perhaps one cannot recognize a thief unless one watches (the crowd), glances (at the front page) or looks (at the intruder), the recognition of the thief is not a matter of success in an observational endeavor. The *purpose* of one's *watching,* even in the case where one happens to recognize, need not be *that* one recognize. It could be very well that one's watching, glancing or looking would be no less successful if no perception of any sort occurred. In a less dramatic example, a person might be in the process of perusing at leisure a book he had not opened for some time, when presently he recognizes a clever illustration which previously had intrigued him, whereupon he lays down the book to think about it. The

process of perusing has ended in recognition, but its satisfaction did not hinge upon any attainment of this sort.
Not only is the recognition incidental to the satisfaction
of the perusing, but moreover the termination of the
perusing is incidental to the recognition. He might as well
have continued to read the book after recognizing the illustration. In like fashion, a microscopist may detect a
virus while scanning a slide under his instrument, but
continue his scanning uninterrupted by the detection.

The first conjecture thus must be rejected. Not only are
observational processes not typically matters of endeavor,
with certain desired results, but moreover when a perceptual act of attainment does occur at the end of an observational endeavor the success of the endeavor may be
incidental to the occurrence of the attainment.

It may be suggested, however, that these difficulties arise
because of clumsiness in the expression of the main point
of C1. The main point, it may be claimed (Ryle seems
rather clear about this as far as his remarks are concerned)
is that the relationship between perceptions and the observational processes which accompany them is not a relationship between two distinct performances, but rather a relationship between doing something in one respect or
fashion and then doing the same thing, or another thing
of the same type, in another respect or fashion. In the
analogy of the race, winning is identical with crossing the
finish line in a certain respect relative to the other runners. And crossing the finish line is to do the same sort of
thing as to cross the half-way and the quarter-way lines,
but these latter (in the course of the race: former) crossings
do not count in the same way in regard to the other runners. The difference between running past the fifty-yard
line and running past the finish line, for the winner, is
that in the one case it is incidental whether other runners
have got there first, while in the other case this matter is

of the essence. Similarly, one might suggest, to perceive an object is to do something of a piece with what one does in watching or looking. Perceiving and looking differ not in being two distinct things we do, but in that one is to do something in one respect while the other is to do the same thing in another respect. These remarks are not precise, but they indicate a promising direction to move in seeking a satisfactory reformulation of C1.

What might be meant by 'doing the same thing in another respect'? That is, when it is said that the difference between X-ing and Y-ing is a matter of doing the same thing in another respect, what relationship between X-ing and Y-ing is being asserted? There seem to be three possibilities. It may be to assert (i) that X-ing and Y-ing belong to the same class (or genus) of acts or activities, but have nothing in common necessarily beyond their class membership. Thus, for example, looking and detecting share membership in the class of perceptual occurrences, or perhaps more specifically in the class of visual occurrences. In this sense, surely, it is safe to say that looking and detecting are to do the same thing (exercise vision) differently. But our problem of clarifying the relation between activities or processes like looking and attainments like detecting began with this observation, and cannot be resolved by repeating it. This first possibility, then, must be set aside as unhelpful.

It may be to assert (ii) that X-ing can be undertaken with or without Y-ing, but that Y-ing is a form of X-ing. In this case, it may be said, when Y-ing occurs so does X-ing, in the sense that Y-ing is just one way of X-ing, which might be done in other ways as well. Y-ing is merely X-ing, carried off in a different fashion from other forms of X-ing, or from X-ing "pure and simple." Some straightforward illustrations could be given of sense (ii).

Consider, for example, traveling (X-ing) and driving (Y-ing). Traveling may be done by walking, flying, or sailing, as well as driving, and when one drives he may either handle the wheel or go along for the ride. Now when one leaves off walking, steps into his vehicle and commences driving, he of course exchanges one activity (walking) for another (driving). But as far as the business of traveling is concerned, he is not doing a different thing before and after taking the wheel. Traveling by driving is traveling nonetheless, and a mark of this fact is that most adverbial expressions which might be used to qualify 'driving' (in the sense of 'going by car' rather than of 'steering') qualify 'traveling' as well without change in sense. We might drive hastily, leisurely, cautiously, hopefully, willingly, apathetically or reluctantly, and when we travel by driving we might travel also in any of these ways. The ways in which we Y are also ways in which we X. (Not all ways in which we X, of course, are ways in which we Y: one might travel first-class, or by air, but driving in these ways, in any literal fashion, is out of the question.) It would seem to be the case generally that if Y-ing is a form of X-ing, then by and large an adverbial expression with which it would be natural to qualify verbs for Y-ing would be available also for use in qualifying verbs for X-ing. As strolling is a form of walking, we might not only stroll, but also might walk, leisurely, purposelessly or confidently. Declaiming is a form of speaking, and we might declaim and also speak heroically, impetuously or shamelessly.

If the suggestion that perceiving is a form of looking is interpreted in this way, it would lead us to expect that most of the expressions which lend themselves to the qualification of perception verbs would apply with similar propriety to at least some observation verbs too. But as has been noted already, this seems simply not to be the case. Although it makes sense to say we had recognized, discerned or detected an object only with luck, it would be strange to speak of viewing, looking at or watching something with luck. We do not scan, listen or glance unexpectedly, but it is commonplace to perceive unexpectedly. An apparent exception: we say 'suddenly he glanced up' and 'suddenly he perceived'. Surely the reply, however, is that the suddenness in the first case is of a muscular and not of a visual process. And it does not make much sense to combine 'suddenly' with other observation verbs, such as 'watching', 'scrutinizing' and 'scanning'.

Observation verbs designate processes, which may be inaugurated suddenly, but not pursued suddenly or abruptly. (We may pursue them swiftly, but this is another matter.) Perception verbs, however, designate occurrences which might be either sudden or abrupt. And so it goes generally for other adverbs that qualify verbs of perception; as a rule they make little or no sense when coupled with a verb of observation. Thus (ii) also must be rejected as an explication of what it might mean to say that to perceive is to do the same thing, but in a different respect, as what is done in looking, watching, scanning or listening.

The phrase 'to do Y is the same thing as to do X' might also be taken to mean (iii) that there is a third thing Z which we do both while doing X and when we do Y. In this case, to say that X-ing and Y-ing are to do the same thing in different respects is to say that X-ing is to Z in one way while Y-ing is to Z in another way. An illustration is at hand with Ryle's remark, quoted above, that to describe a person as having journeyed and arrived is not to say that he has done two things separately but that he has done one thing with a certain upshot. Now the considerations above make it clear that arriving is not *journeying* done in a certain way, much as finding is not seeking done in a certain way. When one finds he has stopped seeking, and when one arrives he has stopped traveling. But when one arrives he likely continues to do a variety of things which he did also when traveling—for example, he continues to walk. The respect in which one walks when traveling by foot is with regard to moving towards a destination, while the respect in which one walks while or after arriving is with regard to relaxing, moving towards another destination or perhaps nothing in particular. To travel may be to walk in a striving sort of way (and we would ask 'Am I on time?', or 'How far have I yet to go?'); to arrive may be to walk in an achieving sort of way (and we ask 'What should I do next?', or say 'That didn't take long'). The formula that perceivings are the outcomes of processes designated by observation verbs may be reinterpreted, along these lines, to mean that perceivings are ways of doing something or another which, when done another way, counts as some sort of observing. While we should be discontent with the suggestion that perceptions and recognitions are the outcomes of lookings and watchings, it is a different thing to suggest that recognitions and other perceptual attainments are the outcomes of activities involved in but not identical with these observational processes. Let us formulate C2 accordingly.

(C2) Attainments signified by perception verbs are denouements of activities which accompany processes signified by observation verbs.

C2 will be defended in the pages which follow. It will be suggested that the activity which accompanies both perceivings and observings is the activity which went under the name 'sensing' earlier in this discussion. This suggestion is at least *prima facie* plausible, since it seems clear that one can neither perceive nor observe, in any of the ways we have been examining, without exercising his sense faculties. It is at least plausible, then, to say that observing is sensing in one way while perceiving is sensing in another way. But before anything more can be said in recommendation of this suggestion, it is necessary to impart precision in what will be meant for our purposes by the term 'sensing'. To do this is the task of the next chapter.

CHAPTER EIGHT

SENSATION
AND PATTERN

1. 'Sight' covers a hierarchy of capacities, some of which might be exercised independently of others. In this respect sight is like speech. To speak, one must (i) be able to utter sounds, (ii) be able to articulate these sounds into speech patterns, and (iii) be able to form these patterns into meaningful speech sequences. Someone (an infant for example) might have ability (i) without ability (ii), and ability (ii) might be present (for example in a two-year-old child) without ability (iii). Moreover anyone capable of (iii) might exercise (ii) without exercising (iii), or might exercise (i) without exercising (ii). But exercise of ability (i) is a prerequisite for exercise of ability (ii), which in turn is a prerequisite for exercise of ability (iii).

Similarly, to see an object one must (1) be capable of visual awareness, (2) be capable of distinguishing visual patterns, and (3) be capable of fixating his attention upon particular patterns which are at least momentarily stable. These are distinct capabilities: (1) might be exercised without (2) or (3) (as with a person on the borderlines of consciousness; James's "blooming buzzing confusion"), and (2) might be exercised without (3) (as a result of phantasy-producing drugs, intoxication, snowblindness or extreme myopia). Exercise of capability (3), however, is dependent upon exercise of capability (2), which in turn is dependent upon exercise of capability (1). The inexercise of capability (3) is visual distraction, the inexercise of capability (2) is visual chaos, and the deprivation of capability (1) is blindness.

There is a correspondence of sorts (not an isomorphism) between these three capabilities of sight and the acts of perceiving, observing and sensing discussed in Chapter Seven. *First,* a percipient who is looking, gazing or scanning an area, but looking at nothing in particular, may be exercising capability (2) without capability (3), although there is no reason why he might not begin to exercise capability (3) also at any time during the process. Exercise of capability (3), however, does not correspond directly to an act of perception. Perception is an attainment, and hence durationless, while the exercise of capability (3) is a protracted activity. Capability (3) rather is among the capabilities necessarily following the perception of an object; for we would say that a person who was totally unable to fixate his attention upon an object has not in fact perceived that object. So we may say, *second,* that perception occurs at the moment of demarcation between the activity of looking for an object (or gazing or scanning, etc.) and the activity of looking at an object, which are respectively the protracted exercise of capability (2) without (3) and the exercise of capability (3) as well. *Finally,* it was suggested in Chapter Seven that perception is the outcome of a "further activity" which accompanies such processes as looking, scanning and gazing, and that this further activity is merely that of sensing. Sensing clearly corresponds to the exercise of capability (1).

In view of this correspondence between the acts of perceiving, looking and sensing on the one hand, and the three capabilities of sight on the other, we may expect to gain information regarding the former by a careful examination of the latter. This sets the purpose of the present chapter.

Now the difference in exercise between capabilities (2) and (1) is that between the presence and the absence of patterns in visual awareness. Similarly the difference between capabilities (3) and (2) is that between the presence and the absence of visual patterns of a certain sort. The concept of *pattern* thus may serve as a focal point in our attempt to explicate the relationships among sensing, observing and perceiving. Like other terms employed in this chapter, 'pattern' has divergent meanings in common and technical discourse. Let us attempt to define the particular use to which the term 'pattern' will be put in the present discussion.

2. A pattern in some respects is like a collection. Just as a collection must comprise more than one distinguishable item to warrant the name, so a pattern is necessarily a pattern of more than one distinguishable element. Although a collection itself might be conceived as a single (abstract) entity, one and only one item cannot itself constitute the entire membership of a collection. And although a pattern itself is a single (perceptible) entity, one and only one element itself (without respect to its parts) cannot manifest a pattern.

The differences are equally important. A collection is a set with a plurality of members. A pattern, to the contrary, although manifest in more than one object, is not itself a set of objects. If an analogy is needed, consider that Congress is more than merely the set of its members. There are relationships among the members beyond common class-membership, and relationships between each of the members and his constituents, which are essential to the identity of the legislative body. Similarly, there are relationships beyond common class-membership among the elements which are essential to the identity of a pattern.

Thus two requirements stand at the beginning of our analysis of the concept of pattern. First, a pattern is manifest in a collection of elements; and second, these elements share within the pattern a relationship beyond that merely of common class-membership. The nature of the elements in perceptually manifest patterns is the topic of the next section. In the present, we consider aspects of the relationship among elements with reference to which we say that these elements manifest a pattern.

Any group of objects within a common system of reference exhibits relationships beyond membership in the same group, but not every group of such objects exhibits a pattern. For example, the cornerstones of all buildings completed during the year 1965 constitute a group of objects, any member of which is spatially related to every other member; but the objects in this group do not exhibit a clear spatial pattern. The several bricks within a particular building, on the other hand, do exhibit a clear spatial pattern. Again, the individual members of a random series of numbers are ordered according to no particular pattern, while by contrast the pattern ordering the progressive series of the powers of two is obvious to any student of mathematics. Similarly, the series composed of the first letter in each of the names of the fifty states arranged according to population shows no perspicuous pattern, while each of the names itself exhibits the pattern of an intelligible word. Finally, the momentary arrangement of bright spots on the screen of a television set out of focus has no discernible configuration, while the screen of a set clearly receiving a broadcast contains numerous meaningful patterns.

The difference between the patterned and the nonpatterned group in each of these cases is not a matter of order or lack of order. Each group in these examples is ordered, for each member of the group can be related to other members within a common frame of reference. The difference rather has to do with the types of order displayed among the members of the group. Stated quite imprecisely, the difference is this: given an arrangement of a subset (*some* subset) of the group of elements, something can be anticipated regarding the arrangement of the remainder of the group. No subset of elements of a nonpatterned group, however, provides a clue regarding the arrangement of the remaining elements within the group. In other words, although the elements of a nonpatterned group can be arranged in some unambiguous order, the ordering is essentially random, while in a patterned group knowledge of the arrangement of a subset provides a basis upon which the arrangement of the remainder of the group might be predicted.

As an illustration, contrast a random series of letters with the sequence of letters within a properly formed word. A random sequence of letters by definition is one in which the occurrence of any letter as a sequel to a given letter in the sequence is equally probable with the occurrence of any other letter. Thus, given the identity of several letters at the beginning of a random sequence of letters, one has no more reason to expect the occurrence of any one letter rather than another in any remaining place within the sequence. In particular, even if someone knows all the letters in a random sequence save the last, he has in this knowledge no more information on which to predict the last letter than he would if he knew only the first letter of the sequence. Given the first few letters of a word, on the other hand, a person who knows the language in which the word is formed often can anticipate correctly that the remaining letters in the word will fall within one of a very few possible combinations. In general, the more letters determined at the beginning of a word sequence, the narrower the range of its possible completions. It is a rare word in which the last letter cannot be determined, or at least narrowed down to two or three possibilities, when all letters save the last are known.

A similar contrast stands between a random and a non-random series of numbers. Given that the first three letters of a series are one, two and four, and given that the series is not random, we would judge normally that there is a higher probability that the fourth number is between five and ten than between 100 and 105; and given that the first five letters of a six letter sequence are one, two, four, eight and sixteen, the probability that the last member is 31 would be considerably less than the probability that it is 32. With a random series of numbers, on the other hand, no differentials of this sort exist among the probabilities of occurrence of later members of the series given any set of earlier members.

The point of these contrasts between random and non-random sequences does not require that the probability of inclusion of a given member be precisely determinable. When the number of possible members within a sequence is small, precise determinations of probable sequents of a given initial series might possibly be made. Given sufficient information about the frequencies of occurrence of various possible letter combinations in a natural language, for example, it would be possible to determine with some accuracy the probabilities of various completions of a word in which the first few letters were known. In the case of number sequences, on the other hand, such determinations could not be made (in the lack of information about the principle, if any, according to which the series is generated), for there are infinitely many possible sequents to any given partial series. This is not important for our discussion of pattern. What is important is that, in general, as our information about the arrangement of part of a pattern increases, the range of probable completions of the pattern which we can anticipate decreases while the range of improbable completions of the pattern increases. This is perhaps best illustrated with the case of the bricks patterned into a building. Suppose that one knew only the location of the cornerstone; given this information alone, one might imagine a very large number of ways in which the remaining bricks within the structure could be situated. But at the same time there would be an infinite number of possible situations which would be excluded by the presumption that the cornerstone is part of a pattern. No part of this particular pattern, for example, would be located 100 miles to the side of, nor ten miles above, that stone. As the positions of more and more bricks within the building become known, moreover, the range of possible ways in which the building might be imagined to be completed would rapidly decrease. Finally, when all save a few of the bricks or stones had actually been set, the position of those remaining could be anticipated with a high degree of confidence.

Let us now attempt to turn these remarks into a definition of 'pattern' which will be sufficiently exact for our discussion. A pattern is an ordering among elements which is such that (1) when the arrangement of a subset of these elements is determined, the range of possible arrangements of the remainder may be subdivided into two (not necessarily exhaustive) ranges of possibilities any member of the first of which is more probable than any member of the second, and (2) in general, as the subset of already determined elements increases with sufficiently large increments, the range of probable arrangements of the remainder decreases and the range of improbable arrangements increases.

This definition accommodates commonplace examples of patterns such as mathematical proofs, musical themes, and ordinary objects like cups and saucers, tables and chairs. Given the first line of symbols in a mathematical proof, or the first note in a musical line, the range of symbols or notes likely to follow is large, but smaller than the range of unlikely symbols or notes; and as more symbols or notes are determined in the sequence, the range of likely elements to complete the configuration is sharply decreased while the range of unlikely elements is sharply increased. Similarly, when a piece of china is situated behind a box so that only an edge appears, it is probable for an observer, on the basis of the information available in the appearance of the partially obscured object, that the remainder when it appeared would exhibit the shape of a bowl, pitcher or cup, and relatively improbable that it should have the shape of a tennis ball, typewriter or telephone; and in general the more of the object that appears, the less likely any of the latter and the more likely one of the former. There are other configurations, of course, which are so improbable initially that any increase in their improbability as more became known about the object would be inappreciable: an object with the edge of a cup, for example, presumably never turns out to have the appearance over-all of a fir tree.

This definition also seems to accommodate up to a point the distinction between *figure* and *ground* of Gestalt psychology. A figure may be conceived as a configuration of elements which manifest a pattern, while the ground for that figure would be the group of elements, neighboring in space and time (but perhaps not proximate to) the elements of that configuration, which are not included within the pattern. Thus the ground of a figure would be composed of those elements (apart from the boundary) which, in being combined in whole or in part with a subset of elements of the patterned group, neither decrease the range of probable completions nor increase the range of improbable completions of that subset of elements within the patterned group. But the conception of a figure as a pattern according to our definition is not entirely helpful. When a shape is delineated within a previously undifferentiated field (as when a cookie-cutter is pressed on a sheet of dough), the shape is manifest both within the field (the remaining dough) and the area marked off from the field (the cookie); hence both the field and the area distinguished from the field are patterned. Gestalt psychologists probably would not want to say that the delineation of a *figure* makes a figure out of its *ground*.

We may return to the main concern of this chapter. It has been suggested that the difference between visual observation and visual perception has to do with a difference in patterns of which the percipient is or might be aware, and that sensing, apart from observing and perceiving, is the exercise of vision without awareness of pattern. It is natural at this point to consider what elements might exhibit the patterns with reference to which these distinctions are made. We shall say that the elements of these patterns are visual sensations. The concept of sensation, however, is notoriously beset with confusion and unresolved problems. Yet it is a very useful if not indispensable concept for such discussions as the present. While it would be unreasonable to require someone who wishes to use the term 'sensation' to resolve or account for all the problems associated with its use in other contexts, he may be expected at least to explain how he intends to use the term. To do so for the present essay is the task of the following section.

3. The term 'sensation' has several technical meanings beyond its various uses in general discourse. It has

been used in physiology and psychophysics, for example, to refer to the response of a system of sensory receptors to stimuli.[1] Psychologists are more likely to use it to refer to the object of awareness elicited when the level of excitation of the receptors exceeds the threshold value.[2] And there is ample precedent in the philosophic theory of perception for using 'sensation' to refer to the awareness itself of a sensible object. It is regrettable that no interdisciplinary conceptual schema has been achieved in which the concepts of sensation as physiological process, as object of awareness, and as act of awareness, can be brought into clear relationship.

In view of this ambiguity in 'sensation', some philosophers have been concerned to devise a terminology of their own in which the structure of sensory perception might be discussed. Among expressions which have been suggested for this purpose are 'sensum', 'sensible species', 'sensibile', 'the given', and of course the old favorite 'sense-datum'. Unfortunately for the philosophic theory of perception, no one has been able to provide a definition of any of these terms which has satisfied the philosophic audience at large, and a great deal of time and space in scholarly journals has been occupied with attempts to show that 'sense-datum', or one of its would-be equivalents, either is meaningless or fails to sustain the use to which it has been put in more constructive phases of the literature.[3] Much of this criticism is justified, for indeed the

---

[1] For examples, see *Receptors and Sensory Perception*, by Ragnar Granit (New Haven, Yale University Press, 1955), p. 9; and "The Difference between Sensing and Observing," by R. J. Hirst, in *Proceedings of the Aristotelian Society*, Supplementary Volume, XXVIII (1954), 215–216.

[2] Frank Geldard seems to use it in this way in *The Human Senses* (New York, John Wiley & Sons, Inc., 1953), p. 115.

[3] A brief survey of the vicissitudes of 'sense-datum' may be found in "Phenomenalism without Paradox" by the present author in *The Concept of Matter*, ed. Ernan McMullin (Notre Dame, University of Notre Dame Press, 1963). Other recent critical works include J. L. Austin's *Sense and*

term 'sense-datum' at one time or another has been put to some extravagant uses.

Yet it has been found difficult to undertake any constructive analysis of sensory perception without the help of some term having roughly the meaning that 'sensation' or 'sense-datum' have often been intended to convey. So too, for our more limited purpose, some term must be provided to refer to those elements which enter in various ways into the patterns disclosed in sensory observation and perception. Let us adopt the term 'sensation' for this purpose, and attempt to avoid at least some of the obscurity associated with this term by providing a particular use which will be maintained throughout the present essay. Let us attempt to provide a sense of the term 'sensation' in which it will be acceptable to say simply that sensing is having sensations, and that observing and perceiving are modes of perceptual awareness in which sensations come to exhibit certain characteristic patterns.

Although our concern is primarily with visual sensing, the use provided for the term 'sensation' should be broad enough to cover deliverances of the other senses as well. So if sensing in general is to be conceived as having sensations, our definition of 'sensation' ought not under threat of circularity refer to the deliverances of sight, hearing, taste, or any other so-called sense faculty as such. Our problem is to locate a feature of the deliverances of sense the description of which is not merely another way of saying that they arise through the activity of sensing. Now one feature shared by the deliverances of sense in general is that they involve some degree of awareness on the part of the human percipient. (There is no reason to think that the senses do not *operate* at times when we are not aware

---

Sensibilia, ed. G. J. Warnock (Oxford, Clarendon Press, 1962), and D. M. Armstrong's *Perception and the Physical World* (London, Routledge and Kegan Paul, 1961).

of their operation; but it seems self-defeating to think of *sensations* of which no percipient is aware.) Sensing is one way in which human percipients exhibit awareness. This is not to say, of course, that along with every act of sensing goes another "act of awareness." It is to say, rather, that sensing is one way in which a person might be aware, other ways being those mental acts which involve reflection, attention, remembrance, and so forth. Let us accordingly tailor our sense of the term 'sensation' to require that sensations involve an awareness on the part of the percipient. But since awareness is not limited to sensing, the concept of sensation must be further specified.

Further specification may be provided with reference to possible objects of awareness. To be aware, in this use of the term, is to be aware of some object or another. But there are many things of many types of which a person might be aware. A person might be aware of justice, of truth or falsehood, of implications or inconsistencies, of meanings, of nuances, of intentions or of commitments. Again, one might be aware of books, chairs, trees and other material objects. One might be aware further of tones, shades of color, pressures of various intensities, degrees of warmth, and similar matters of qualitative distinction. Now things like justice, truth and meanings, whatever their status among things that are, are not objects of sensory awareness. We do, however, speak of sensing both things like books and chairs and things like tones, shades and degrees of warmth. Awareness of the former is clearly different from awareness of the latter. Let us side-step the many distinctions that have been or might be drawn between objects and qualities, and attend to the fact that we attribute properties of weight, shape and physical dimension to material objects but not to sensory qualities. Properties of weight, shape and dimension, of course, are among those traditionally called "primary

qualities" and now sometimes called merely "quantities."
And one of the distinguishing marks of a quantity is that
it has features which cannot be determined specifically by
the "naked eye" or by other unaided observation alone,
but which require measurement of some sort for their
specification. Thus one does not tell whether a figure is a
square or a nearly-square rectangle by looking at it alone,
but rather by measuring its sides or by comparing it with
a known square of comparable size. And one does not determine the weight of an object merely by lifting it or by
pushing it along the floor, but rather by subjecting it to
some appropriate procedure of weighing. The point here
is that, although procedures of weighing and measuring
and the like are applied in the context of situations in
which we are aware of the object being weighed or measured, the procedures of measurement themselves include
more than merely being aware of the object. So there are
some features of material objects which are not manifest
specifically in our ordinary awareness of the objects. This
seems to be a consequence of that conception of material
object according to which material objects necessarily
possess one or more of the so-called primary qualities.

A mark of tones, shades of color, and pressures, on the
other hand, is that none of their features is hidden from
unimplemented sensory awareness. The pleasant tone (not
configuration of sound waves) is one in the awareness of
which a person is aware of its being pleasant; the sharp
pressure (not probe applied to the skin with a certain
amount of force) is one in the awareness of which a person
is aware of its being sharp; and similarly, although degrees of warmth and shades of color can be correlated with
thermometer readings and areas on color spindles, the
features of the warmth or color which we attempt to corre-
late are apparent within our unaided awareness of the
quality. It is with reference to sensory objects of this sort

that we shall attempt to specify our use of the term 'sensation'.

The relationship between sensations and such "secondary qualities" as colors, sounds, and tastes, however, is not so direct as theorists of sense perception have sometimes surmised. It would be a mistake, for one thing, to *equate* sensations with colors and the like. We say (tautologically) that red is a color, and that red is the property which all red things have in common. But the property which all red things have in common is not a sensation, for sensations are not properties of objects. We shall want to say, moreover, that colors and the like are not in themselves among the *objects* of sensations. Paradoxical as it may at first seem, there are reasons for thinking that we are never aware of red, or of any other color or similar quality, without at the same time being aware of another quality of the same sense modality with which that color can be contrasted. Let us attempt to elucidate these reasons in the context of a few simple thought experiments.

Now one case in which we might be tempted to say that a person *is* aware of one and only one color is when his eyes are shut and have not been exposed in the immediate past to strong illumination. It might be tempting to think in this case that the person is aware only of black. The fact that there may be reasons in color theory for denying that black is a color is not necessarily a deterrent to this way of thinking. But there are reasons quite apart from this why it seems preferable to say that the person in this case is aware of no color at all. When a person's eyes are shut, and there are no afterimages, "floating spots," or other manifestations of his "color imagination," that person's sense of vision simply is not active. Instead of saying that he is aware only of black, we should say that he is aware of nothing at all. This much seems obvious. Now let us consider what differences there might be between this and some similar situation in which it would at first seem appropriate to say that a person is sensing only red, or any color other than black alone. It will not do, for one thing, to suggest that some people "see only red" when their eyes are shut, whereas most people supposedly "see only black." Not only is there no way an external observer could distinguish between a person's "seeing only black" and a person's "seeing only red" when his eyes are shut, but moreover there is no way the percipient himself could make this distinction. If there is no contrast between colors within a percipient's field of visual awareness, there is no basis on which he might judge that one color rather than another is present within his awareness. If he has a vivid "color imagination," of course, so that he could "remember" what red looks like, he might be able to make a comparison with this image; but if an image of this sort is present in addition to the color with which it came to be compared, we would not say that the percipient is aware of one color only. And if only an image of this sort were present, the situation would be the same as before: he would have no basis on which to judge the color of this particular image.

Insofar as this line of reasoning is persuasive, it might be applied as well to situations in which we would be tempted to say that a percipient whose eyes are open and properly functioning is aware of one and only one color. Now there clearly are cases in which one's field of visual awareness is dominated by one color or another. In a uniformly lighted room with red walls, floor and ceiling, and with no windows and no visible fixtures or other furnishings, a percipient certainly would be aware of red; there is a sense, moreover, in which he might be said to be aware of red *only*. But we would say this only in the sense in which 'red' covers a variety of shades and tones of color which are discriminately different. The percipient in the red room will be aware of many shades and tones of red, and the reason he is able to be aware of any one of these is that he is able to discriminate it from some other shade or tone within his field of awareness. If, by some master stroke of engineering, all differences of hue were made to disappear within the room, there would be nothing in the behavior of the subject to enable an external observer to distinguish between his "seeing only one color" and his having suddenly gone blind. And if there were no contrast between colors within the subject's field of awareness, his situation would be the same, even though his eyes might be open, as that of the person with his eyes shut who has no way of judging whether one color rather than another is present within his awareness. Since neither an external observer nor the subject himself could judge what color might be present to him, or even whether any color is present to him, it would seem the better course simply to consider that the subject is aware of no color at all. The "field of awareness" of the subject in such a circumstance is like a "picture" which contains absolutely no contrast of color or form. At very least there would have to be some contrast between the "picture" and its frame or the wall behind it; otherwise there would be no object to which the term 'picture' (even with boundless tolerance from the critics) could be applied. Similarly, if there is no contrast of any sort within an observer's field of visual awareness, there is no reason to say he is aware of anything at all.

Let us say, then, that to be visually aware is to be aware of contrasts within one's field of vision. To be aware of only one color is to be aware at least of two shades or tones both of which, due to the generality of our color vocabulary, we call by one color name. To be aware of many colors is to be aware of at least that many contrasts within one's field of visual awareness. The person who is entirely color-blind is visually insensitive to any contrast except that between various shades of gray, while the person who is color-blind with respect to red and green is aware only of those contrasts which can be set up between the remaining shades and tones to which he is sensitive.

If these remarks are accurate, we will want to say that visual sensing is not the awareness of colors, but rather is the awareness of various qualitative distinctions of a chromatic sort. Sensations of colors accordingly will not be conceived as awarenesses of colors simply, but will be conceived rather as awarenesses of distinctions with regard to various color shades, tones and intensities.

Let us accordingly define the term 'sensation' to refer to an awareness of qualitative distinctions. If these distinctions are marked by differences of color, the sensations are visual; if marked by differences of sweetness, bitterness and the like, the sensations are gustatory; if marked by differences in pitch, loudness or timbre, the sensations are auditory; and so forth for the various other senses. The question of how many senses a percipient has is just the question of how many different unrelated ranges of qualitative differences there are to which that percipient is sensitive.

This definition does not eliminate the need for an independent understanding of the vocabularies of color, sound, taste and the like. It assumes rather that these vocabularies are already meaningfully established. But it does not depend upon a prior understanding of the expressions 'visual sensing', 'tactual sensing', 'auditory sensing' and the like; consequently the term 'sensation' can be used in a definition of sensing without circularity. Let us define sensing to be the act of having sensations. To sense, then, is to be aware of qualitative distinctions.

It does not follow from this concept of sensing that the difference between sensing and sensation is merely the difference between act and object. Sensing indeed is an act; but the object of sensing is not a sensation or series of sensations. The objects of sensing, rather, are the objects presented within the awareness of the observer in sensation. Since the objects of awareness in sensation are qualitative distinctions, these too are the objects of sensing. An analogy which might be helpful here is that of the relationship between drop-kicking as the specialty of a particular player and the particular drop kicks which he makes in pursuit of his calling. What is kicked with a particular drop kick is a ball. And what is kicked in the act of drop-kicking clearly is not a particular drop kick, but rather is the same ball or balls kicked with particular drop kicks. Drop-kicking is the making of drop kicks, and accordingly the object of drop-kicking is the same or of the same sort as the object of a particular drop kick. Drop-kicking here is analogous to sensing, and the particular drop kick is analogous to a particular sensation. Just as the objects of sensations are qualitative distinctions, the object of an act of sensing is a qualitative distinction or array of such distinctions. It should be apparent then that the object of sensing is not a sensation or array of sensations. This is a departure from the once popular notion that sensations (or sense-data) are objects uniquely accessible to acts of sensing, existing actually or virtually in some mysterious realm distinct from the realm of everyday objects. The objects of sensing, in the present way of thinking, are of a garden variety, no more (and no less) mysterious than the detectable differences between various colors, various odors or various sounds.

Since a sensation is an awareness of a particular sort, and since an awareness is not a material object, it follows that sensations themselves do not have the spatial and temporal features characteristic of material objects. This is not to deny, for example, that particular sensations occur before or after other sensations; there unquestionably is a serial ordering of sorts within our sensory awareness. It is to say rather that individual sensations, apart from their relationships with other sensations, do not themselves admit temporal characteristics. Although an awareness of qualitative distinctions might be located in time relative to another awareness (as when someone exclaims 'there's another flash'), the awareness considered as an individual occurrence has no temporal dimension. The case with respect to spatial features, however, is not so perspicuous, due to an ambiguity we have thus far tolerated regarding the "number" of qualitative distinctions that can be present to the awareness within a "single" sensation. It appears on empirical grounds that we often are aware simultaneously of a variety of qualitative distinctions; and it is not clear, from anything said previously, whether this awareness should count as one sensation in which several qualitative distinctions are present, as more than one sensation some one or more of which is an awareness or are awarenesses of more than one qualitative distinction, or as several sensations each with only one qualitative distinction. If either of the first two alternatives were chosen, phenomenological reasons could be marshaled for arguing that sensations contain within themselves differences at least with regard to spatial ordering: some qualitative distinctions within the field of awareness might be in front of, behind, above, below, or to the side of other qualitative distinctions within the same field. The very dreariness of this puzzle, however, suggests that it is one which simply should not be allowed to arise. The *number* of an object or group of objects is a property that is of a sort with weight, shape, size, and other "primary qualities" which usually are taken by definition to belong exclusively to material objects, and which have been expressly excluded from the present characterization of sensations. Although there is no reason to hesitate in speaking of an awareness of the present moment as a different sensation from an awareness an hour ago, there is no basis either in the conceptual analysis or in the empirical investigation of sensations to assign a definite number to the various sensations of which an observer might be aware at a given time. To ask how many sensations a percipient might have during a given moment, or to ask for an analysis into components of the various qualitative distinctions that might be present within one sensation, is to betray a confusion about the nature of these distinctions. The point of calling them "qualitative" is that they do not admit "quantitative" characterization.

There are reasons, in fact, for declaring that sensations simply cannot be analyzed at all. First, since sensations have no structure in space or time, it makes no sense to speak of dividing them into constituent parts. The point is not that the awareness of a percipient at a given moment lacks a variety of sensory objects, but rather that we have no justification for thinking of these various objects as parts in some part-whole relationship. Since we cannot ask how many qualitative distinctions constitute a given portion of our sensory awareness at a given moment, we cannot single out a particular sensory object to ask whether it is part of a more inclusive whole (rather than being, for example, a whole in itself). Second, if an observer were to attempt to analyze the elements within his visual field at a given time by some procedure of "inward concentration," from the very moment he began the contents of his immediate awareness would begin to give way to others. What he had attempted to analyze would no longer be available for analysis by the time the analysis (in whatever form) had got under way.[4]

---

[4] The present point is a denial that individual sensations can be analyzed into further individual sensations, and is in agreement with what R. B. Braithwaite has said in this general regard: "When I am hit on the head, my visual sense-field becomes one which, though it has no distinct

Finally, if sensations could be analyzed, it would be the case surely that they could be analyzed both correctly and incorrectly. And if sensations could be analyzed incorrectly, it would be the case that the percipient could be misled in his awareness of qualitative distinctions, or at least that he could make a mistake in estimating the nature of the qualitative distinctions present within his awareness. That this be possible in turn would require that the objects of sensory awareness have features which are not disclosed in ordinary sensation, but rather which could be displayed only through some sort of (perhaps conceptual) implementation. In our attempt to elucidate the concept of sensation, however, it was taken as typical of the objects of sensory awareness that they have no such features. If our field of awareness contains objects subject to analysis, it contains objects which exhibit some sort of pattern and which hence are not objects of sensory awareness alone.

It is undeniable that people often are misled through sensory observation. We are misled when in looking through a mirror we estimate that we are looking through a window, or when in glancing at a cigar box in the shape of a book we expect to find printed pages upon opening the cover. What is misleading in such cases is not the sensations themselves which are involved, but rather the patterns in which the sensations are structured or appear to be structured. Individual sensations lay no claims with respect to further experience. But when sensations fall into

---

parts, is heterogeneous in the sort of way that makes it appropriate to describe it by a plural noun. When I discriminate distinct parts (e.g., to take a most striking case, when I "resolve" the sound of a note on the piano into a fundamental and harmonics), I am not discriminating parts within a whole which all the time contained these parts undiscriminated, but am changing one sense-field into another" (review of A. J. Ayer's *Foundations of Empirical Knowledge,* in *Philosophy,* XVII [1942], 87). It seems clear, nonetheless, that individual sensations can sometimes be distinguished within our awareness of patterns of sensations, as in the exercise of capabilities (2) and (3). See fn. 5 below in this regard.

patterns in the process of sensory observation, we are led by everyday experience to anticipate further sensations within these patterns. And in this respect we frequently are misled. It is time to return to our consideration of the differences between observation and perception, with regard now to the parts played by sensations within these two modes of perceptual activity.

4. Sensing and observing have been associated respectively with the capabilities (1) of sensory awareness and (2) of distinguishing patterns within a sensory field. Perception has been associated in turn with the capability (3) of fixating attention upon stable patterns. But whereas sensing and observing were correlated with the exercise of capabilities (1) and (2), perception was not correlated with the exercise of capability (3) but rather has been conceived as an attainment following which that capability might be exercised. Since our conception of the differences among these three capabilities involves the concept of pattern, we have attempted to provide a definition of 'pattern' in terms of which these differences could be more fully explored. And since the concept of pattern is engaged with the concept of element, we turned next to consider the elements involved in patterns exhibited within a sensory field. The ambiguous but perennially useful term 'sensation' has been interpreted to provide a means for referring to these elements. The task remaining for this chapter is to elucidate the differences among capabilities (1), (2) and (3), and thus to elucidate the distinction among sensing, observing and perceiving, with the help of the concepts of pattern and of sensation thus defined.

Sensing, the exercise of capability (1), has been defined as the activity of having sensations. Since each sensation is an awareness of a qualitative distinction, there can be distinguished conceptually within the structure of a sensation both a mental attitude and the object of that attitude. But sensations are not analyzable in any further sense which would warrant thinking of them as patterns; in particular they have in themselves neither a temporal nor a spatial dimension in which a pattern might be exhibited. A sensation then is an unpatterned element in a sensory field, and sensing is the awareness of unpatterned elements.[5]

Although sensations do not exhibit patterns, they may serve as elements in patterns exhibited either spatially or temporally. Let us illustrate these possibilities with reference to various perceptual attitudes one may take towards the display on a radar scope. An inexperienced viewer of a radar scope might be aware only of individual spots or groupings of spots; in such an act his awareness, being one

---

[5] To call a sensation an "unpatterned element" should not suggest that sensations cannot be elements in patterns. The point rather is that sensations as such do not exhibit patterns within their structure. It should be clear also that to speak of sensations as elements of patterns does not commit us to an "atomism" in which sensations are unalterable constituents of acts of "higher awareness." It appears, to the contrary, that the character of sensations is affected in some fashion by their entry into the patterns exhibited with the exercise of capabilities (2) and (3). No attempt has been made in this chapter to elucidate the way in which this is so. Help might be expected here from phenomenology, from experimental psychology (see for example Ulric Neisser's "Visual Search" in *Scientific American* [June 1964], pp. 94–102), and even from the social sciences (see "Analysis of the Concepts Whole, Differentiation, and Unity," in Kurt Lewin's *Field Theory in Social Science* [New York, Harper Torchbooks, 1951], pp. 305–338). Another disclaimer also may be appropriate at this point. Although we have suggested that exercise of capability (2) depends upon exercise of capability (1), and that exercise of capability (3) depends upon the exercise of capability (2), it certainly is not the case that exercise of capability (2) requires two separate perceptual acts or that exercise of capability (3) requires three separate perceptual acts. There is no more reason to say that this is so than to say that the articulation of sounds into speech-patterns requires two distinct vocal acts since it depends upon the utterance of sounds. We have claimed, indeed, that there is a sense in which awareness of unpatterned elements (at level (1)) is implicated in awareness of patterns (at levels (2) and (3)). But this is no more than to claim that one cannot be aware of a pattern without in some sense also being aware of its elements.

of a qualitative difference between light and dark areas, provides an example of a sensation. In this awareness the spots or groups of spots take on no particular configuration and hence exhibit no pattern. When in the awareness of a more experienced observer these contrasts between light and dark areas are focused into a spatial pattern which can be taken in "at a glance," we say that the observer is scanning the face of the scope. In this process of scanning the observer may remain unaware of any persistent configurations, either because none is exhibited on the face of the scope or because none has attracted his attention. The patterns of which he is aware have spatial characteristics, but since they do not endure they lack temporal characteristics. When it happens, however, that the observer's attention is fixated for a time upon some particular configuration of spots persisting upon the scope, we say that he has noticed or detected what may be an aircraft data-trail, a prominent land-mass or perhaps an area of unusual electronic activity. Subsequent to this detection he may attend to both the spatial and the temporal features of the pattern upon which his attention has been fixated. Before detecting the persistent configuration the viewer's attention has been limited primarily to spatial characteristics of patterns on the scope face. After detecting the configuration he is alert not only to its spatial features but also to its features as a continuing pattern. In another example, while a lookout on shipboard scans the horizon looking at nothing in particular (but looking *for* approaching aircraft) his sensations are organized into spatial patterns but are not organized notably in a temporal fashion. Thus the contents of his field of visual awareness at one moment do not lead him to anticipate the appearance of any particular configuration of sensations during following moments. But when he spots a prominent moving object his attention becomes fixated and he follows its movement for some appreciable period of time. During this period he is led to anticipate its movement through successive locations on the basis of his awareness of its movement during previous moments. If his anticipation of the object's continuing movement is even initially successful, we would say he had detected the moving object.

When the attention of the inexperienced observer of the radar scope is directed primarily towards unpatterned sensations, his perceptual activity is limited primarily to the exercise of capability (1). When the observer attends primarily to spatial patterns of sensations within his field of awareness, as when the experienced operator views the scope or when the lookout scans the horizon, he is perceptually involved primarily in the exercise of capability (2). And when for a time his attention is concentrated upon a particular configuration of sensations which he is concerned to follow, trace out or further observe, he is exercising capability (3) as well. At the moment his attention becomes concentrated in this fashion upon a stable or otherwise persistent configuration, we say he has espied, detected, recognized or in some other way perceived that configuration or an object associated with it. (We may say indifferently, for example, that the scope operator has detected a data-trail or that he has detected a moving object.)

This use of the notions of spatial and temporal characteristics is geared to the concept of pattern. Now a percipient's field of awareness may in a sense exhibit both spatial and temporal characteristics even though his perceptual activity is limited to the exercise of capability (1). At any given moment he may be aware of qualitative distinctions some of which appear to be oriented to the side of, above or behind others. And presumably there is a temporal dimension exhibited within any percipient's field of awareness as he continues to sense from one moment to the next. With the exercise merely of capability (1), however, these spatial and temporal characteristics are not exhibited in *patterns* of sensations. That is, they are not such that consideration of the spatial or temporal features exhibited with respect to some of the qualitative distinctions of which the percipient is aware will lead him to anticipate spatial or temporal features exhibited or about to be exhibited with respect to other qualitative distinctions within his field of awareness. Similarly, when a percipient is exercising capability (2) but not capability (3) he may nonetheless be aware in some sense of temporal relationships among the spatial configurations to which he is attending. The radar scope operator, even while merely scanning the scope, may well be aware, as it were, of the passage of time within his general field of awareness. And such surely would be the case as well with the lookout observing the area just above the horizon, but attending to no one particular object from one moment to the next. The reason we should consider such cases to be examples of the exercise of capability (2) exclusive of capability (3) is that any temporal features which may happen to be exhibited within this awareness are not characteristics of configurations of sensations which lead the observer to anticipate further characteristics exhibited by those configurations, or extensions of those configurations, as they may appear subsequently to the observer. Anticipation of the characteristics of future configurations on the basis of presently observed configurations of sensations rather is the mark of the exercise of capability (3).

It is clear that the exercise of capability (3) is not itself an act of perception. To be aware of a configuration from one successive moment to the next is a protracted activity, one in which there are earlier and later phases and one in which a person may be successful in one phase while relatively unsuccessful in another. In a word the exercise of capability (3) is a process. Since perception is an attainment, it cannot be directly correlated with capability (3), as observation is correlated with capability (2). Perception rather is to be conceived as an attainment subsequent to which it is essential that the percipient be able to exercise capability (3) in an appropriate fashion appropriate to the occasion of perception. Thus if a person is unable through a period of time to focus his attention upon any continuing pattern within his field of awareness, we would want to say that he had not perceived anything during that period or during the moments immediately preceding. We would deny as well that he had detected, recognized, discriminated, descried or in any other way come to the point of a perceptual attainment during that period.

These remarks do not amount to a definition of the acts of observing and perceiving. Our purpose in making them rather is to elucidate the relationship between acts of observing and acts of perceiving with reference to the three perceptual capabilities distinguished in this chapter. It is interesting to note that the distinctions among observing and perceiving when thought of in this way remain generally faithful to the distinctions drawn from the bits of conversation at the beginning of Chapter Seven. Let us provide a context for each of these remarks. (i) If someone is attending carefully to the sounds around him on a calm summer evening but is unable to focus his attention upon any *enduring* sound which might occasion the question from his companion, "Listen carefully; what's that?", he might reply "I *am* listening carefully, but I don't hear a thing." (ii) When one is gazing over the hills and plains below from a vantage point on a mountain peak and one's companion asks "What do you discern?", it may be appropriate to indicate that no particular object had *caught* (and held) one's attention by replying "Nothing; I'm just enjoying the view." (iii) When two children are hiding from the farmer some of whose apples they have just pilfered and who is peering around in the dark attempting to discover the culprits, one may reassure the other that the farmer's gaze did not *dwell* upon them by whispering "He glanced in our direction, but I don't think he noticed." (iv) "Watch carefully, and report to me the moment you detect anything" might be words issued to a radar scope operator by his commander, in which he is instructed to scan his scope continuously and to report the moment a *stable* pattern of data appears within the display. To hear, to discern, to notice and to detect, as the terms for these acts are used in these brief scenes, in each case is to apprehend a configuration subsequent to which apprehension the percipient's attention is directed towards its stable or regularly developing spatial and temporal characteristics.

Let us return briefly to the second conjecture of the previous chapter for its vindication. It is part of C2 to assert (1) that certain activities accompany the processes designated by observation verbs such as 'look', 'see' and 'scan', and (2) that the attainments signified by perception verbs are among the outcomes of these activities. The activities common to observing and perceiving are those of sensing. Observing is sensing within the structures of spatial patterns. An attainment of perception occurs at that moment in the process of sensing at which sensations become organized within patterns which are both spatial and temporal in structure. In this respect perceiving is the outcome, but not the termination, of the activities of sensing which lead to the percipient's awareness of these spatial-temporal patterns.

The concept of perceptual attainment cannot be divorced from the concept of pattern in our thinking about human perceptual behavior. This will seem to be the case as well when we turn in Part Four to thoughts about the perceptual attainments of mechanical systems.

CHAPTER NINE

RECOGNITION
AND PERCEPTION

1. The term 'recognition' will be used henceforth to refer to a mental act which occurs in intimate association with perception. With this use it is a necessary truth that a person who recognizes an object also perceives or has perceived more or less recently the object he recognizes. An example of recognition occurring simultaneously with perception is provided by a person who recognizes a tulip tree "at a glance," or who recognizes a friend's voice immediately upon hearing it. But recognition occurs also in the case of a person who puzzles for a while before an untitled picture in a gallery and then passes on, only to recall the title and recognize the picture in a moment of idle thought after having left the room. In this case it is clear that the person recognizes the picture on the basis of his perception of it, but that he did not perceive the picture at the very moment of recognition.

Restriction of the term 'recognition' to situations in which the object recognized is seen, felt or in some other way perceived is in accord with our primary focus upon recognition of letter-patterns, for there is no occasion to speak of letter-pattern recognition which might occur independently of perception. At the same time it is apparent that the term 'recognition' has a wider application in ordinary contexts of a different sort. There are objects which in another sense of the term can be recognized but which are not ordinarily given in sense perception. A military leader might recognize victory in the denouement of his campaign without in any sensory way perceiving that desirable outcome. A logician might recognize the validity of a proof, or the relevance of an assumption, without in any way perceiving (as against conceiving) the proof or the assumption. But given the present topic, it may be excusable to pass by the complication that would arise if our concern were extended to the recognition of matters which, like relevance, validity or victory, are not accessible to sense perception.

Although it is a necessary truth that a person who recognizes an object perceives or has perceived that object as well, it is not necessarily the case that a person who perceives an object also recognizes that object. Although both 'recognition' and 'perception' refer to acts of attainment, they do not refer to the same acts. We have examined in previous chapters various respects in which the concepts of recognition and of perception are similar. It is time now to consider various equally important respects in which these concepts differ. We have noted that to recognize an object is at least to perceive that object or to have perceived it more or less recently. But it is something more as well. By examining the differences between recognition and perception we may hope to discover the missing term of the formula: 'to recognize is to perceive or to have perceived, and in addition to . . .'. To supply this missing term is the purpose of the present chapter.

2. We turn first to some of the more apparent differences between recognition and perception.

(a) According to the theory outlined in Plato's *Meno* and *Phaedo,* acquisition of knowledge is a matter of *re*collection or *re*cognition. As someone comes to know that about which he has been ignorant, he "cognizes again" something of which in some sense he had previously been aware. This stress on the first syllable points up something which seems to be true of recognition generally, namely that *re*cognition presupposes *pre*cognition. Apart from the intricacies of Plato's theory, it seems that one may properly be said to recognize only something which, as it were, one has previously cognized. If I have never seen, been told about, read about or in some other way come to know about gooseberries, then upon seeing a gooseberry for the first time I scarcely could be said to recognize it. The next time I see a gooseberry I probably will recognize it, if not by name then at least as an object of the sort I had seen some time previously. But if the first time one perceives an object is the first time one has ever been cognitively aware of such an object, perforce at that time one does not *recognize* it.[1] It is commonplace, on the other hand, that we *perceive* objects which we have never perceived before, nor learned about in any other way. Sense perception, in fact, is a primary source of information about novel objects. In short, although it is normal to perceive novel objects, a person would not normally be said to recognize an object which is like nothing he had ever known before. This is one of the more obvious differences between perception and recognition.

(b) The claim that someone who has no previous in-

---

[1] There may appear to be an exception in the case of an amateur botanist who, upon seeing a flower of a certain sort for the first time in a field, returns to his manual and finds it illustrated, thereupon remarking "*Now* I recognize it." He claims to recognize the flower, having seen it only once, without having other information about the flower prior to that time. This apparent exception is accommodated in the following discussion.

formation about gooseberries would not be said to recognize a gooseberry the first time he sees one requires clarification. Although a person in these circumstances would not recognize a gooseberry, it might well be that he would recognize a berry of *some* (unknown) sort, and it is very likely indeed that he would recognize the object to be a thin-skinned fruit rather than a leaf or a nut. When a person *perceives* a berry which is in fact a gooseberry, it is equally true to say that he perceives a berry and to say that he perceives a gooseberry. But to say truthfully that a person *recognizes* a berry which is in fact a gooseberry does not require that it be true as well to say that he recognizes a gooseberry. This is another difference which will turn out to be significant in marking out the distinction between perception and recognition.

It may be helpful to make this point in terms of the venerable notion of generality of reference. The term 'vertebrate', for example, has a more general reference than the term 'mammal', which in turn has a more general reference than 'whale'. Consider that Jones is looking at a whale, and that it is true to say (using 'see' as a verb of perception) 'Jones sees a whale'. This being the case, it necessarily will be true also to say 'Jones sees a mammal' and 'Jones sees a vertebrate' (as well as 'Jones sees a living creature' and 'Jones sees a physical object'). This is the case, not because of some particular fact regarding the nature of Jones' visual awareness at the moment, but because of the logical connections among the terms 'vertebrate', 'mammal', and 'whale'. Consider, on the other hand, that it is true to say 'Jones recognizes a whale'. It does not follow from this that it is true also that Jones recognizes a mammal, or even that he recognizes a vertebrate.[2] If Jones

---

2 'Perceive' in this regard is like 'buy', 'catch' and 'eat': to buy, catch or eat a lobster is to buy, catch or eat a crustacean, whether or not the agent knows that a lobster is a crustacean. 'Recognize', however, is more like 'typify'. Although Tartuffe typifies a hypocrite, and all hypocrites are men, Tartuffe does not typify a man.

knows that whales are mammals, of course, presumably he would recognize a mammal when he recognizes a whale. But imagine that Jones does not know this. Whether Jones recognizes a mammal or a vertebrate when he recognizes a whale is more than a matter of the logical connections among the terms 'vertebrate', 'mammal' and 'whale'. It is a matter involving as well what Jones in particular happens to *know* about these connections. This point may be put more formally: if A, B, and C are terms so connected that all A's are B's and all B's are C's, then the statement 'Jones perceives an A' entails in turn the statements 'Jones perceives a B' and 'Jones perceives a C'; but the statement 'Jones recognizes an A' does *not* entail either 'Jones recognizes a B' or 'Jones recognizes a C'. Insofar as A is less general in its reference than B, and B than C, this point regards what might be called "ascending degrees of generality."

A similar difference holds in regard to *descending* degrees of generality. Let the terms A, B and C be related as above, so that C has a more general reference than B, and B than A. Then the pair of statements 'Jones perceives a C' and 'This C is a B' entails 'Jones perceives a B', etc. But the statements 'Jones recognizes a C' and 'This C is a B' do *not* entail 'Jones recognizes a B'. If, to change the example, it is true to say both 'Jones perceives a bird' and 'This bird (that Jones perceives) is a finch', then it is true to say also 'Jones perceives a finch'. But it is not the case that 'Jones recognizes a bird' and 'This bird (that Jones recognizes) is a finch' together imply 'Jones recognizes a finch'. Jones might know this is a bird without knowing it is a finch, in which case it would be true to say he recognizes a bird, but false to say he recognizes a finch.

(c) The distinction above suggests another difference between recognizing and perceiving which at first glance seems entirely straightforward. A person may truthfully be said to perceive an object even though he does not know what the object is. But it seems not to be the case that a person who does not know what an object is can be said truthfully to recognize the object. It is not necessary, of course, that one know everything that might be known about an object in order to be able to recognize it. There are many things most men do not know about internal combustion engines, although most men certainly can recognize internal combustion engines. What is necessary is that one know *that* an object is an internal combustion engine if it is to be said truthfully that one recognizes an internal combustion engine upon looking at the object. But not even this is necessary for it to be true to say that a person perceives an internal combustion engine when he looks at one. We perceive many things we do not recognize. And the difference between perceiving with recognition and perceiving without recognizing would seem to be one between knowing and not knowing what an object is that one perceives.

The distinction here may be put schematically. If x is an object at which person O is looking, then 'O recognizes x' and 'O does not know what x is' exhibit an incompatibility which does not appear with the pair of expressions 'O perceives x' and 'O does not know what x is'. If Jones does not know that a particular bird is a finch, this is no bar to the claim that Jones perceives a finch while looking at the bird. But it could not be said truthfully in this case that Jones recognizes a finch as he looks at the bird.

The relation between recognizing an object and knowing what it is appears so intimate as to suggest that the difference between perceiving and recognizing an object is merely that in the latter case one must know what the object is while in the former this is not necessary. But the notion of knowing what an object is covers various abilities a person might possess relative to the object he knows. And it might be that some of these abilities are essential to recognizing the object while others are not. Let us attempt to find a more precise sense of 'knowing what a thing is' with the help of which the difference between recognizing and merely perceiving can be formulated.

Now one respect in which a person might be said to know what a thing is has to do with his ability to name or to classify the object in point. Thus one knows who a new neighbor is when one learns his name, and one knows what a flower is when one can classify it according to species. Let us consider the following conjecture regarding the missing term in the formula above:

(C3) To recognize an object x is to perceive or to have perceived x and in addition to be able to name or to classify x.

This conjecture asserts a sameness in meaning between the conjunction (a) and (b)

(a) O perceives or has perceived x
(b) O is able to name or to classify x

and the statement

(c) O recognizes x.

The significance of this conjecture is intended to be such as to render it subject to the following informal test: if the conditions under which the reader would take (c) as true are invariably the conditions under which and only under which he would take the conjunction (a) and (b) as true, then he will accept (C3); otherwise he will reject it.[3] Since any of the three statements may be either true (indicated by writing '(a)', '(b)' or '(c)') or false indicated by writing '(ā)', '(b̄)' or '(c̄)'), there are in all eight possible

---

[3] This test applies only to statements which are neither inconsistent nor tautologous. Otherwise we would be led by it to attribute sameness of meaning to all logical truths (or all logical falsehoods), either separately or in combination.

combinations of truth values. When these are arranged
as below, the test may be stated as follows: if there are any

(a)	(b)	(c̄)		(a)	(b)	(c)
(a)	(b̄)	(c)		(a)	(b̄)	(c̄)
(ā)	(b̄)	(c)		(ā)	(b̄)	(c̄)
(ā)	(b)	(c)		(ā)	(b)	(c̄)

conditions which the reader can conceive under which he
would count any one of the conjunctions in the left-hand
column true, or all the conjunctions in the right-hand
column false, the reader will reject C3; otherwise he will
accept it. The first conjunction in the left-hand column,
for example, appears false under one interpretation at
least, for there would seem to be no conditions under
which we would say that (a) one perceives an object and
(b) can name the object, but that (c) one does not recognize
the object.

Now it would be tedious at best and impossible at worst
to attempt to verify the conjecture by this test. But this
does not matter, for our concern is to use the negative
criterion provided by the test. Consideration of the second conjunction to the left alone will disclose reasons for
rejecting C3. According to C3 it must always be false to
say that someone perceives an object he cannot name or
classify but that he recognizes it nonetheless. But there are
circumstances of a garden variety in which this is just what
we would want to say. The average gardener, for example,
often encounters pests which he cannot name and which
he cannot even classify correctly as insect, larva or worm,
but which he quickly recognizes as the bugs which have
been eating his vegetables.[4] People whose houses are being

---

[4] It may be tempting to say that the gardener here can *classify* the bugs
as those which have been eating his vegetables. This description, however, does not furnish a principle of classification. *Other* bugs may also
be eating his vegetables, but would not be grouped with these in his
recognition. To describe is not necessarily to classify.

chewed by black insects may not know whether they are victims of termites or carpenter ants, but although they cannot name or classify the insects will not hesitate to claim that they can recognize a specimen of the marauder when one appears. In a word, the fact that a person cannot name or classify an object does not in itself invalidate a claim to have recognized the object.

C3 therefore must be rejected. But the notion of knowing what a thing is might be taken also to cover the ability to identify an object or type of object.[5] Ability to identify an object does not require so much of our knowledge about an object as does ability to classify it correctly. In the examples above, the gardener surely would claim to be able to identify the pest that was eating his vegetables even though he could not classify it, and the householder is able to identify the insect which has been chewing his home even though he is unable to supply its name. What seems inadequate with these examples in regard to C3 can be set right if the phrase 'ability to identify' is put in place of 'ability to name or to classify'. We surely would want to say that if one can in no way identify a thing one sees, perforce one does not recognize it; conversely if someone is able to identify a thing, if not by name then with reference to his previous experience of the thing, we would want to say that he has recognized it. Let us consider this relationship between recognizing and being able to identify in the form of a further conjecture:

(C4) To recognize an object x is to perceive or to have perceived and in addition to be able to identify x.

The claim of C4 is that the conjunction (a) and (b′)

---

[5] The closely related concepts of classification and identification were distinguished in Chapter Six. The differences between them will appear larger from this point onward. In the discussion which follows, 'identify' is taken to refer to the process of supplying a description rather than to the attainment of finding a missing object.

    (a) O perceives or has perceived x
    (b′) O is able to identify x

has the same meaning as the statement

    (c) O recognizes x.

C4 is recommended at least by its being not susceptible to the difficulty which defeated the initially plausible C3.

Another consideration in favor of C4 is that it goes a considerable way towards explaining the differences between perception and recognition which were noted at the beginning of this section. It is entirely plausible to say, for instance, that the reason one cannot be said to recognize an object about which one has no previous information is that some previous information about an object is necessary if one is to be able to identify it. To speak of identifying something concerning which one has no previous information seems entirely nonsensical. Since a person need not be able to identify an object in order merely to perceive it, however, there is nothing strange about the claim to perceive something concerning which one knows nothing previous to perception.

The second difference (b) also receives illumination in light of C4. To perceive a whale is *ipso facto* to perceive a mammal, and to perceive a bird which is actually a finch is to perceive a finch. But to recognize a whale is not necessarily to recognize a mammal, and to recognize a bird is not necessarily to recognize a bird of some particular species. The reason for this would seem to be simply that the ability to identify a whale, which is essential for recognizing one, does not carry with it necessarily the ability to identify a mammal, nor does the ability to identify a bird carry with it the ability to identify a finch.

The third difference (c), of course, was what initially suggested C3 and subsequently C4; it would be illuminated retroactively if C4 could be shown tenable.

3. Another point in favor of C4 is the intelligibility it lends to a further difference between the terms 'perception' and 'recognition' which in itself is rather remarkable. Austin has noted what he called an "asymmetry" among certain verbs, notably those used in certain obviously performative utterances.[6] The verb 'to promise', for example, conveys a meaning in the first person ('I promise') which does not carry over in the second and third persons (neither 'you promise' nor 'he promises' effects a promise). Now the verb 'to recognize' is asymmetrical in two respects similar to this, and in neither respect does it share its asymmetry with 'to perceive' or synonyms of this latter term. This asymmetry focuses around a peculiarity of the expression 'I do not recognize . . .'. The peculiarity is this: when the name of an object is inserted in the blank, the resulting statement is one which, barring insincerities and misrepresentations, is invariably true.

Let us note first that the verb 'to perceive' behaves rather normally in this respect. The statement 'I (do) perceive a goldfinch', of course, could be either true or false, depending in part upon whether I am looking at a bird which is in fact a goldfinch. If the bird I perceive is indeed a goldfinch, as claimed by my utterance 'I perceive a goldfinch', then the utterance is true. If it is not a goldfinch (but, say, a canary instead) then the utterance is false. Similarly, to say 'I do not perceive a goldfinch' would be to make a true statement if the bird I am looking at is not actually a goldfinch. And if I *were* looking at a goldfinch, even though I thought it was a canary, that statement would be false. Either possibility is conceivable. And this is the case quite apart from the possibility of lying, from utterances with the express purpose of exemplifying phil-

---

[6] See for example *How to do things with Words*, ed. J. O. Urmson (Oxford, Clarendon Press, 1962), p. 68. Other philosophers also have been aware of this feature in some verbs (for example, Wittgenstein, as evidenced by private records of some of his lectures).

·osophic points, and from other comparably exceptional utterances, all of which are meant to be excluded from this comparison. I could be right in claiming either to perceive or not to perceive an object of a particular type, but I could be wrong in either claim as well. The admission 'I think that I do not perceive a finch, but I could be wrong' is a disclaimer which is perfectly intelligible, insofar at least as it means (i) I perceive what I take to be a bird, (ii) I think it is not a finch, but (iii) my estimation in this latter regard may be mistaken.

The verb 'to recognize', however, does not permit so wide a range of intelligible formulations. The utterance 'I recognize a goldfinch', parallel to what is the case with 'I perceive a goldfinch', could be either true or false under very ordinary circumstances. If the bird I perceive is not a goldfinch the utterance is false. If it is a goldfinch, and (according at least to C4) if I can identify it as such, then the utterance is true. The assertion that I do *not* recognize a goldfinch, on the other hand, admits only one truth value when made in the mode of discourse which normally characterizes assertions (barring exceptional cases as noted above). If I claim ingenuously not to recognize an object of a particular sort, I *do not* recognize such an object. When someone claims he does not (cannot) recognize an object, there is no room left for another person (who believes the first is not fabricating) to reply that the first does, after all, recognize the object whether he thinks so or not. The utterance 'I think I do not recognize a finch, but I could be wrong' has no use, at least when it is taken (parallel to the example above) to mean (i) I perceive what I take to be a bird, (ii) I think I do not recognize it as a finch but (iii) my estimation in this latter regard may be mistaken. To say 'I think I do not recognize the bird' is to say that in fact I cannot recognize it. There appear to be no circumstances in which a person could be said, as it were, to be surprised by "actually recognizing" something which at the same time he thought he did not recognize.[7]

The asymmetry we have just noted arises in regard to the truth values admitted by assertions beginning 'I (do) recognize' and 'I do not recognize'. The second asymmetry has to do with the person of the pronoun with which the verb 'to recognize' is used. Whereas '*I* do not recognize . . .', as we have seen, would normally be used to express a true but not a false assertion, '*he* does not recognize . . .' could begin an assertion which could be either true or false under circumstances which are quite easy to conceive. The assertion 'he recognizes a goldfinch' might be true if the person 'he' refers to is looking at and perceiving a bird which is indeed a goldfinch, and it certainly would be false if the bird is not. Similarly, to say 'he does not recognize a goldfinch' would be a true saying if the bird at which he is looking is not a goldfinch. But the assertion that he does not recognize a goldfinch could be false as well. The person who makes the assertion beginning with the pronoun 'he' might simply be mistaken in his estimation of what the person to which the pronoun refers does or does not recognize. The disclaimer 'I think he does not recognize a goldfinch, but I could be wrong' could be put to intelligible use in quite ordinary circumstances. (Consider: "I think he doesn't recognize Jamie; I certainly *hope* not. But we'd better be ready to run just in case.")

On the one hand we find that utterances beginning 'I recognize . . .' could be either true or false while those beginning 'I do not recognize . . .' could only be true. On the other hand we find that utterances beginning either with 'he recognizes' or 'he does not recognize' could be either true or false. The asymmetry in both cases is at

---

[7] See fn. 4 of Chapter Six.

least partly explained by C4, according to which the claim
to recognize an object includes the claim to be able to
identify the object in the circumstances of the utterance.
The claim *not* to be able to identify an object is one in
turn which, if uttered without dissimulation, could only
be true. If I claim not to be able to identify a bird, then
indeed I cannot identify it.[8] There is no evidence or
further information beyond that upon which I make my
claim which would tend normally to reverse the truth
value of my claim itself. In a word, there is no room in
such a situation, barring dissimulation and mental aber-
ration, for saying that a person can identify a given object
at a given time when in the person's own estimation he is
sure he cannot. He might *later* be able to identify an object which previously had eluded him, but this is an entirely different case. When a person *claims* at t_o that he
cannot identify an object, then this is the best reason conceivable, assuming a sound mind and good intention, for
saying he *cannot* identify that object at t_o. Thus, a person's
claim on his own behalf not to be able to identify a goldfinch at a given time is in a sense incorrigible. It could
not be wrong, because no evidence normally would be
available which would have the tendency to contravert it.
Consequently, upon C4, a person's claim on his own behalf *not* to recognize a goldfinch shares the same incor-
rigibility. 'I do *not* recognize that bird', uttered in any
straightforward context, could not be false. But since I
could be wrong in claiming to be *able* to identify a goldfinch (if what I see instead is a canary), I could be wrong
as well in the claim that I *do* recognize such a bird. Similarly, *my* claim that *you, he,* or *she* cannot identify an

---

8 One may be *uncertain* about his ability to identify an object or objects
of a certain type, in which case he would not normally say he *cannot*
identify it or them. The claim here is that when one *says* without reservation that he cannot, then indeed he cannot.

object can be contraverted by an actual identification on the part of the other person; so consequently can my claim that you do not, or he or she does not recognize the object.

4. The concept of *seeing as* has received considerable attention recently among philosophers, while that of *recognizing as* has gone unnoticed. We can learn about these two concepts by noting contrasts in their logical structures. Since our present concern is primarily with recognition, no attempt will be made to review everything that has already been said about *seeing as*. (In keeping with the terminology of the present discussion, the expression 'perceiving as' could be substituted for 'seeing as' in most of the illustrative phrases below. This is not to enter a claim of complete equivalence for these two expressions: in some cases, in fact, the result of this substitution would sound rather odd. In each use below, however, 'see' is used as a verb of perceptual attainment.)

The point has been made by Wittgenstein and others that a person does not see an object merely *as* the object it is. This seems correct, at least insofar as it means that there is something odd about saying (for example) that someone sees a shoe as a shoe. One might see a shoe as a fine piece of leather, as a status symbol or as a foot-covering. But it is difficult (perhaps not *impossible*) to think of a situation in which there would be any point in describing what goes on by saying 'He sees the shoe as a shoe'. I might see Laurence Olivier as Hamlet, but not Olivier as Olivier, nor for that matter Hamlet as Hamlet. But this restriction does not carry over into the deployment of the concept of *recognizing as*. To recognize a shoe as a shoe, in fact, seems to be just the right thing to do. It may be appropriate to recognize a shoe as a foot-covering, a status symbol or a good piece of leather; but it is no less appropriate to recognize it as a shoe as well. To recognize a person for what he is, is to take an x for an x; and to recognize an x as an x and say so is "to call a spade a spade." Although I would not be inclined to describe anything I do, or might do, as "seeing Olivier as Olivier," to *recognize* Olivier as Olivier might be a desirable accomplishment. This is one difference between *seeing as* and *recognizing* as.

Another difference is with regard to the truth conditions of locutions manufactured out of these two expressions. The statement 'John sees that shoe as a fine piece of leather' might be true even though the leather is actually inferior. (Compare this with 'John sees her as a beautiful woman, when actually she is quite plain'.) But the statement 'John recognizes this shoe as a fine piece of leather' would normally count as true only if the leather is as described. 'He sees a bird as an airplane' could be either true or false, depending primarily upon his visual and/or mental attitude more than upon the bird. 'He recognizes the bird as an airplane', on the other hand, seems neither true nor false, but rather a poorly-constructed sentence. Someone who said this seriously would do so only through misunderstanding of the concept of *recognition*. For something to be recognized as an airplane, it must *be* an airplane. A person might mistakenly take a bird for an airplane, and claim thereby to have recognized an airplane, but what we would say in that case is not that he recognized a bird as an airplane, but that his claim to recognize an airplane is false. In a word, if it is true to say that someone recognizes an object as an x, then it must be true to say also that the object *is* an x; by contrast, the truth of the statement that someone sees an object as an x leaves entirely open the question what in fact the object is.

It should be noted that the expression 'see as' functions quite differently from the term 'see' in this regard. The statement 'John sees a bird' is on a par with 'John recognizes this object as a bird' as far as truth conditions are concerned, and so is the statement merely that John recognized a bird. For any one of these three statements to be true, it is necessary that the object at point (which John sees, or which it is claimed he recognizes) in fact be a bird. Thus, in this regard, 'see as' stands in contrast not only with 'recognize as' but also with merely 'see', while 'recognize' by itself shares the logical characteristic in point with the latter two expressions.

These differences between *seeing as* and *recognizing as* can be illuminated with reference to the involvement between recognition and the ability to identify which is asserted by C4. Before turning to this, however, let us note one further difference between the two expression-schemata 'to see x as y' and 'to recognize x as y'. (Both are proper when the meanings of the terms substituted for 'x' and 'y' are not identical.) The first format would be most likely to be in evidence in statements where the expression, y, is a description or interpretation of x from a particular point of view, under a particular light or with a special interest involved. Thus, it might be said 'John saw the missile as a threat' when the missile was flying in John's direction (but not when flying away from him), or 'John saw Olivier as Hamlet' when John was in the audience (but not when John was in the street). The seeing of x as y indicates that a particular ("special," although not necessarily unusual) construction or interpretation has been put upon x. This, of course, is tied in with the fact noted above that it is not necessary that x in fact *be* y in order for it to be true that x is seen as y. To recognize x as y, on the other hand, constitutes a *specification* of x (or perhaps of y: to recognize a whale as a mammal) rather than in any clear sense an *interpretation*.[9] And this in turn is tied in with the point discussed earlier in this chapter that when a per-

___

[9] This does not conflict with the previous suggestion that it is sometimes proper to speak of recognizing an object (x) for what it is (x). The point here is that *when* x is recognized as y then either y specifies x or (occasionally) x specifies y.

son recognizes an object A which is also a B he may or may not recognize a B as well.

Consider, for example, what might be said about my recognition of a bird which is a goldfinch and which is, moreover, the mother of the bird in the nest outside my window. It might be true to say merely that I recognize a bird upon perceiving this creature. It might be true moreover to say that I recognize a goldfinch, in which case it would be correct to say I recognize the bird *as* a goldfinch. If my vision were especially acute, it might even be correct to say I recognize the bird, or the goldfinch, as the mother of the bird in the nest. In either case, to recognize the bird as so-and-so is to achieve a specification in my recognition of the bird. To recognize the bird as a finch signifies not an interpretation of what I perceive but rather an increase in my knowledge about what I perceive. Recognizing the bird as a goldfinch, I am able to say more about it than if I were to recognize it merely as a bird. The sense in which recognizing x as a y adds up to a specification of my recognition can be put more formally with the help of the schema 'O recognizes _____ as . . .'. If the first but not the second blank can be filled in, that is if O recognizes _____ but not as anything in particular, then it can be said merely that O recognizes _____. But whenever the second blank can be filled in correctly, it will be possible to fill in the first blank as well. The term fitted into the first blank need not necessarily be the "proximate genus" of the term in the second. I may not know that this object which I recognize as a whale is also a mammal. But at least I will know that it is an aquatic creature. So at least it could be said that I recognize this aquatic creature as a whale.

What is in point here obviously is the degree of specificity of my knowledge about what I recognize. And this brings us back to the matter of being able to identify the object which one rightly can claim to recognize. To be able to identify a bird does not imply ability to identify a goldfinch, whereas ability to identify a goldfinch does imply ability to identify at least some birds. When I am perceiving a goldfinch which I am able to identify only as a bird, I do not know as much about this object I perceive as would be the case if I could identify it as a goldfinch as well. Thus being able to recognize the bird as a goldfinch represents an increase over the knowledge of this object which I would have if I were able to recognize it merely as a bird of no particular type. This point may be put by saying that I have a more specific knowledge about the bird which I can recognize as a goldfinch than about the bird which I can recognize merely as a bird.

The equation, according to C4, of recognizing an object with perceiving the object and being able to identify it, adds intelligibility as well to the two points of comparison between *seeing as* and *recognizing as* discussed earlier in this section. In light of C4 we would want to say that *recognizing* a bird *as* a bird is a matter both of perceiving (or having perceived) a bird and of being able to *identify* the bird *as* a bird. Whereas to speak of *perceiving* an x *as* an x borders on nonsense, recognizing an x as an x shares characteristics relevant in this regard with identifying an x as an x. What is desired in setting out to identify an x is precisely to achieve an identification of it *as* an x. Similarly, it is perfectly proper to speak of recognizing an x as an x.

The second point of comparison between these two concepts was that to recognize an object as an x entails that the object actually is an x, whereas to perceive an object as an x does not share this requirement. The explanation of this difference is routine if C4 is admitted. To perceive an object as an x is to construe it in a particular way, and whether or not a person construes the object in this way is a fact not about the object but about the person himself. It is not required, in short, that the object *be* an x in order for a person to take it as one in his perception of it. But to recognize an object as an x requires by the very meaning of the term 'recognize', if C4 is correct, that the recognizer be able to identify the object as an x. This is possible in turn only if the object in fact is an x, since it is obvious that an object can be identified only as what it is and not as something else.

The conjecture that recognition of an object is equivalent to perception of that object given the ability to identify it thus is in accord with the major points in our discussion of the differences between recognition and perception. We turn finally to consider the ways in which the ability to identify an object which one perceives or has perceived might add up to recognition of the object in various concrete circumstances.

5. To identify an object in the sense of the term 'identify' here relevant is a process the outcome of which is to provide a proper designation or description for the previously unidentified object. To be *able* to identify an object is to be able to provide a proper designation or description. Now there are various senses in which an individual might be said to be able to identify a person, place or thing.[10] In one sense it would be intelligible and usually true to say of any intellectually and perceptually competent person that he can identify mushrooms. 'You too can identify mushrooms' is at least a conceivable title for a manual giving instructions for telling on the basis of observable characteristics the difference between edible varieties and toadstools. What the title would allege is not

---

[10] Ryle distinguishes a wider variety of uses of dispositional terms than are discussed here. See G. Ryle's *The Concept of Mind* (New York, Barnes and Noble, Inc., 1949), pp. 126 ff.

of course that the reader (whoever he may be) can at the moment identify mushrooms but rather that the reader can *learn* to identify them. In this sense, 'to be able to x' means more exactly 'to be able to learn to x'. This clearly is not the sense in which a person must be able to identify an object in order to recognize it upon seeing, hearing or in some other way perceiving it. For a second sense, consider that any competent chemist is able to identify a sample of nitrogen gas. To possess this ability again is obviously not enough to warrant the claim that a particular chemist *has* recognized (merely "on sight") any sample of nitrogen gas he may happen to have perceived. If he is actually to recognize a given sample, it would be necessary for him to have undertaken certain procedures of analysis which he very well might not have undertaken in connection with the sample in question. He is able to handle these procedures in a routine fashion; hence he is able easily to identify the sample. But this ability in itself still is not enough to found the claim that he has recognized the gas merely upon encountering it perceptually. Similarly, we would want to say that the person who at first glance did not recognize the painting in the gallery, but who recognized it shortly after leaving the room, was capable of identifying the painting even while perceiving it. He had learned enough about the painting previously to acquire this capability. His inability to identify the painting upon sight was merely a momentary lapse in this capability. But this lapse was enough to prevent his recognizing the painting at the moment of perception. At that moment he was indeed unable to provide the correct designation of the painting. When that ability returned he thereby came to recognize the painting.

The sense of the term 'ability' then, in which a person must have the ability to identify an object in order to recognize it, is one which concerns his competency to provide a proper designation or description at the very moment of recognition. If this competency is present at the time the person perceives the object, that is the time also when he recognizes it. It is often the case, however, that this competency is regained some time after the object in point has been perceived. In such a case, the moment of recognition is not the moment of perception but rather the moment at which the competency returns. Thus with the example of the painting we say that the viewer recognized the painting shortly after having left the room where he saw it, but that he did not recognize the painting while looking at it previously. Like all perceptual attainments, recognition is a datable occurrence. The time at which recognition of an object occurs is either the time at which the object is perceived or the time at which the perceiver becomes able actually to identify the object, whichever is later. This accounts for the possibility of recognizing an object at some time after the moment at which the object is perceived.[11]

It should be emphasized that recognition of an object does not require that the object *actually* be identified, either at the moment of perception or thereafter. It is not necessary that the visitor to the gallery who later becomes able to identify the painting he had seen hanging there actually *articulate* an appropriate designation or description of the painting in order to recognize it. It is enough that he be able to do this. The chemist who recognizes sulphuric acid immediately upon smelling it is able on the

---

[11] It also accounts for the possibility mentioned in fn. 1 of this chapter that a person might recognize an object having seen it only once. Subsequent to seeing the flower in the field for the first time, the botanist becomes able to identify it when he has located the illustration in his manual, at which time it seems appropriate for him to say 'Now I recognize it'. Note, however, that it remains inconceivable that a person should recognize *immediately* upon sight an object of which he had not been cognitively aware previously.

basis of that perception to identify it. He is able, that is, to answer 'sulphuric acid' to the question 'What is it?' or to give another appropriate response to another form of questioning the identity of the fluid sample. But it is not necessary that the occasion for saying anything of this sort arise in the context in which we would say that he recognizes the fluid. If he in fact provides the identification, it follows that he is able to do so and hence that he actually recognizes the fluid which he perceives or has perceived. His not *uttering* the terms of identification, however, is no bar to his having recognized. It is enough that he is able to do so if and when the occasion arises within the situation of his perceiving the fluid.

These remarks constitute a deployment of the concept of identification beyond that in Chapter Six where identification was contrasted with recognition and classification. The notion of *ability* to identify has been entered into the account. And it may be objected that there remains something puzzling about the notion of an ability to identify which need not necessarily be exercised in order to warrant a claim to recognition. It is sufficient defense for our present purposes to remark, in anticipation of developments to come, that no reliance upon unexercised abilities is involved in the specifications of the mechanical letter-recognition system provided in the final chapter below. By way of a more general defense, perhaps it is relevant to note that there is no incompatibility in claiming to recognize an object which one never actually names or describes, whereas it does indeed seem incompatible with the claim to recognize to say that one is simply *unable* to name or to describe the object which one claims to recognize.

The considerations of this chapter have not demonstrated that C4 is correct. It is not clear indeed how a conjecture of this sort *could* be demonstrated. These considerations have perhaps shown, however, that C4 has sufficient explanatory power to justify the recommendation that it be accepted as a point of departure for our further discussion of the concept of recognition, as we come to consider the problems of the mechanical simulation of recognitive behavior.

PART IV

THE

RECOGNITION

OF

LETTER-

INSCRIPTIONS

CHAPTER TEN

THE PROBLEM
OF CRITERIA

1. An act of perceptual attainment is something like a home run in baseball. If a home run is made at all, it is made in a proper fashion; and if something in the process of trying for a home run miscarries, we say that no home run in fact has been made. Just as there are no bulls-eyes which miss the mark, so there are no home runs which are not properly executed. It is in this sense also that perceptual attainments are not liable to incorrect performance. And since the recognition of letter-inscriptions is a perceptual attainment, it follows that there is no act which would count as the incorrect recognition of a letter-inscription.

This does not entail that the *claim* to recognize (or to have recognized) a letter-inscription is never incorrect. Although the act of recognition itself cannot miscarry, the judgment that recognition has occurred can be either true or false. We are often able, as a matter of fact, to distinguish between a correct and an incorrect claim to recognition by observing the behavior of the person for whom the claim has been entered. When a person claims correctly to have recognized a letter-inscription, we would expect something about his behavior to be detectably different from what it would have been if his claim were incorrect.

The recognition of letter-inscriptions itself cannot be incorrectly performed. Yet if a person has indeed recognized a letter-inscription, there should be something he does which he *could* do improperly but which, by being done properly, marks the difference in that case between recognition and the failure to recognize. Between the time just before recognition and the time just after a person recognizes there should be some aspect of that person's behavior which changes in a detectable way. And whatever this change might be, it would count as an important part of the difference between this person's recognition and his failure to recognize. The problem of characterizing this change amounts to the problem of establishing a criterion by which the recognition of letter-inscriptions in practice can be distinguished from perceptual behavior which falls short of recognition. The problem of establishing this criterion sets the task for the present chapter.[1]

2. The question of the criterion of letter-recognition is an important one for our purposes. For whatever the behavior may be which marks the distinction between recognition of letter-inscriptions and failure to recognize, this is the behavior which we would expect a successful letter-recognition mechanism to simulate. And there is a

---

[1] If, as has been suggested, recognition is conceived as perception of an object which the perceiver is able to identify, the present problem may be construed as the problem of finding a behavioral criterion for this ability. Since recognition of an object can occur without *actual* identification of the object perceived, there is no compelling reason here to feel that the ability to identify *must* have a behavioral criterion. Yet if we cannot specify a detectable difference in behavior between a person who recognizes an object he perceives and one who does not, little success can be claimed for our efforts to understand what it is to simulate human recognitive behavior.

related point of practical importance: unless we are able to specify a criterion for distinguishing between recognition and failure to recognize, we will not be able to distinguish clearly between successful and unsuccessful attempts to simulate the performance of letter-recognition by human beings.

This is one of the consequences of a fuzzy and inaccurate conception of recognition which is particularly unfortunate on the part of simulation specialists. A person's estimation of what is essential in the distinction between recognition and failure to recognize depends upon his conception of what it is to recognize. If there are basic mistakes in a person's conception of recognition, it is unlikely that he will be able to say precisely what would count as a successful simulation of recognitive behavior. Indeed, he might not even be able to evaluate meaningfully the success or failure of a particular simulation experiment with which he might be involved. An example of this comes out of the confusion between recognition and classification which is so prevalent in current literature on pattern-recognition.

When the concepts of recognition and classification are assimilated, it is natural to think of a successful recognition mechanism as one which is successful at some sort of classification. In particular, it is natural to think of a successful letter-recognition mechanism as one which correctly classifies a certain high proportion of all letters presented to it for processing. Thus, if a machine classifies as A's all and only those symbols presented to it which are in fact A's, all and only B's as B's, and so forth, and if the machine is consistent in this performance for well-formed and for poorly-formed letters alike, then according to this way of thinking it would be considered a highly successful letter-recognition mechanism. Correct classification becomes the criterion for recognition. If a person or mechanism correctly classifies a given letter, the person or mechanism will be considered to have recognized the letter, while failure in classification will count as failure to recognize.

This is a signally unfruitful way of thinking about the difference between recognition and the failure to recognize. Apart from the confusion between recognition and classification, it involves the questionable assumption that we are able to make a distinction between the correct and the incorrect classification of particular letter-inscriptions which does not involve at least an implicit reference to their being recognizable. The notion of the correctness of a classification, rather than providing a criterion, itself calls for a criterion in order even to be intelligible when applied in connection with letter-inscriptions. Before exploring these difficulties, however, let us observe how the "criterion" of correct classification might function in a particular case.

L. D. Harmon, in reporting an interesting experiment with the mechanical recognition of letters in cursive script, writes that his method

> was tested by processing 19 sentences (412 letters total) written by five persons. The correct letter-identification for the entire group was 58.9 per cent. The best result for one sentence was 81 per cent, the worst was 33 per cent.[2]

In this experiment, the letters to be recognized were entered into an IBM 704 computer by means of an "electronic pen" which communicates its motion to the computer in terms of x, y coordinates. The persons providing the samples were instructed to write their letters carefully and legibly, and relative to a given base line. Identification consisted in classification of the letters according to

---

2 "Machine Reading of Cursive Script," L. S. Frishkopf and L. D. Harmon, in *Information Theory*, ed. Colin Cherry (London, Butterworth and Co., Ltd., 1961), p. 313.

a set of five " 'local features' which are common to a large selection of reasonably legible handwriting samples."[3] Given this input to the recognition system, we can reasonably surmise that the output was evaluated somewhat as follows. For each letter entered into the system, the computer responded with an indication of its identity. If and only if the computer's identification agreed with that of the writer or that of the experimenters, the computer was credited with a correct identification. Finally, the correct and incorrect identifications were tallied, and the proportion of correct identifications announced as the result of the particular test in question.

At first glance there appears to be nothing unreasonable about this procedure. But let us consider a few questions which it suggests. We might wonder first what the results tell us about the ability of the system as a recognizer of letter-inscriptions. Why are the figures interesting? The machine has a range of successful classifications varying from 33 to 81 per cent. Does this mean that in its best performance the machine was only 19 percentage points away from complete success? If so, one would expect the experimenters to push on for a higher percentage of correct classifications. Let us imagine that the system has been improved to give 95 per cent correct classifications over a series of experiments involving, for example, one dozen writers. Should we consider that the attempt to simulate human letter-recognition now is almost completely successful? What we would be justified in thinking is that the machine produced classifications of several letters which agreed in nineteen out of twenty cases with the identifications provided by the dozen people who wrote them. It undoubtedly would be an accomplishment to build a machine which could do this. But we are free to

---

[3] *Ibid.*, p. 301.

ask exactly what relevance such a machine would have to the task of building a mechanical system which performs comparably to human beings in the recognition of letter-inscriptions. If we were told of a human being who over a series of tests agreed in his identification of letters with twelve other human beings, but with no others or with only a few others, we probably would not agree that this person could recognize letters in any ordinary sense. And if we did not know whether this person could agree in his identifications with others beyond the twelve in the experiment, we would want reasonable assurance that his performance with this dozen is typical before we would consider without reservation that he has normal capabilities of letter-recognition. The case of the mechanical recognition system is no different in this respect. Only if the writing of the twelve people during the experiment were a fair sample of "writing in general" would these results indicate success in the attempt to simulate human letter-recognition. And we would have no reason a priori to consider it a fair sampling, regardless of who the twelve were and of how they had been instructed to write, since different people are likely to form their script characters very differently indeed. It seems unlikely in fact that a machine which agreed 95 per cent with twelve people part of the time would agree with most people most of the time in a fashion suggestive of the capabilities of the normal language user. There is nothing beyond the obvious in these remarks. But we have yet to understand the significance of reports such as that of Harmon that "the correct letter-identification for the entire group was 58.9 per cent."

The situation of 95 per cent correct classification is unreal, and contains a further obscurity which can be brought out as well in connection with the 81 per cent correct classification actually reported for part of the experiment. One way of interpreting this latter result is that the machine returned *the* (one and only) correct identification of 81 per cent of the letters during part of the experiment. But this does not seem immediately helpful, for the expression '*the* correct identification' does not have an obvious meaning in this application. It would be less misleading to say merely that the machine agreed in its identification with that of the writer in 81 per cent of the letters. But from this it does not follow that the machine was 81 per cent *correct,* for there is no reason to think that the writer of a letter is necessarily correct in his identification. It would seem, of course, that the writer of a letter normally is in the best position to identify the letter, particularly if it is in a context the meaning of which depends upon a particular identification. But will it do to take the identification of the writer as a *criterion* for the "true identity" of a given letter? It appears that it will not do at all, for there are many conceivable situations in which the identification of the writer could sensibly be challenged. This would not be possible if the writer's identification itself is the criterion for "what the letter is."

Imagine some situations in which the identification of the writer would be problematical. Suppose, for example, that the writer entered a figure into the system which he claimed to be a lower case A, but which every other person present could see only as an O. Suppose moreover that one of the onlookers pointed out that the stroke flowing from the top of the figure came nowhere near the base line as it should in a lower case A; but the writer still insisted that the figure was an A. Now imagine a more extreme case, in which the question 'Is it really a . . . ?' becomes even more puzzling. The writer marks a wavy horizontal line with the "electronic pen" and claims that the computer has made a mistake because it did not identify the mark as the sequence of letters 'I-N-G'. Would not the onlookers be justified in defending the computer, despite the insistence of the writer that this is the way he writes 'I-N-G'? Or suppose that the writer forms a figure which looks like an 8, but which he calls a lower case G, and that the computer surprises everyone present by identifying it as a G. The writer claims that the computer was correct, while several onlookers claim that the computer was mistaken because it did not identify the figure as a numeral 8. It would seem more natural to side with the majority in such a case. But we would be more hesitant to insist that the figure is an 8 if a number of additional observers, selected at random, agree with the writer that the figure is instead a G. But should we not resist the inclination to think that the number of people who agree in their identification of a particular figure has any essential bearing upon what the figure "really is"? Why should the opinion of a larger group of people be any more a criterion for the "true identity" of a letter than the opinion of a smaller group? What percentage of persons present, or of all possible language users, would be necessary to give the opinion of the majority clear precedence over the opposite opinion?

It is clear that this whole line of questioning is misdirected. Recognition is not classification; hence recognition is not *correct* classification. It is not 51 per cent correct classification, nor is it 100 per cent correct classification. The notion of "correct classification" does not provide a key for resolving our puzzlement about the criterion of recognition. In fact, as long as we are unable to say precisely how the identity of a letter-inscription is established, the notion of correct classification poses its own problem of criterion. People *do* classify letters correctly; this has never come into question. But our ability to do so often seems to be consequent upon our recognition of the letters in point. The temporal order in our exercise of these abilities is just the reverse of what would be the case if recognition were (or were the result of) correct classification. Instead of recognizing because he classifies correctly, a person is able to classify correctly because he recognizes. Indeed, if a person is not able to classify a letter correctly, we would probably want to say that he has not recognized it. But, as in the case of the novice stock boy who classifies automotive replacement parts according to their stock numbers alone, there is often nothing amiss in speaking of a person who can correctly classify items he fails to recognize.

Our preliminary concern with the problem of finding behavioral manifestations of the difference between recognizing a letter and perceiving but not recognizing a letter has led back to the conceptual impasse of Chapter Three. There we saw reasons for believing that the distinction among the various letter-inscriptions associated with our written alphabet is a matter neither of their shape nor of their topological characteristics. From the considerations immediately above it is clear also that the distinction is not to be drawn merely with reference to the opinion of the writer or to a majority opinion of the users of the language or languages in which the associated letters occur. But it would be intolerable if the problem of distinguishing among inscriptions of the various letters were left at this impasse. After all, people do both recognize and identify letter-inscriptions with ease and reliability. There must be *something* unique about each of the various letter-forms associated with our alphabet which accounts for this ability.

Thus our present problem of criterion merges with the problem of Chapter Three, and we have instead a problem of criteria. First, we wish to distinguish between the behavior characteristic of a person who recognizes a letter and the behavior of a person who perceives the letter but does not recognize it. Second, we want to specify whatever it may be that enables a clear distinction to be made among inscriptions of each of the various letters. These are separate problems. But, as we have seen, they are related; and it may be that in the process of looking for a solution to the first, a solution to the second as well may begin to appear. As a first step, let us re-examine, with the help of a somewhat more technical vocabulary, the difficulties of specifying the characteristics which distinguish the various letters of our alphabet.

3. Letter-recognition in human beings is a transaction involving a reaction to particular symbols. Whether etched in sand, chiseled in granite, or written on paper, each letter-symbol is distinct from every other symbol. It is distinct even from other symbols which we would say are "of the same letter." The term 'letter', in fact, betrays an ambiguity which must be brought into the open. We speak, on the one hand, of a letter as a mark inscribed, etched, or chiseled on a writing surface. On the other hand, we speak of the fact that many such marks are symbols "of the same letter." The referent of the term 'letter' in the first use is to a particular physical object. Reference in the second use, however, is to something entirely abstract. Logicians in recent years have marked these two uses, respectively, with the terms 'token' and 'type'.

Transit companies in several metropolitan areas still issue small metal discs worth the amount of one fare. These are called "tokens," with reference perhaps to their function of representing a value distinct from their worth merely as pieces of metal. The term 'token' has a similar use in connection with letter-symbols. In the context either of transportation or language, a particular token is one of many discrete physical objects representing another object which is both singular and abstract. Thus there are (indefinitely) many different letter-tokens for any one letter-type, while letter-types, in the Roman alphabet, total twenty-six. Each letter-token has a unique physical location at a given moment, while letter-types have position only in a timeless sense relative to their serial order in the alphabet. There are, for example, five letter-tokens in the first printed word of this line, two of which are tokens of the same letter-type. These two tokens, however, are quite distinct from each other and from the tokens in the corresponding position on the present page of other copies of this book. These several letter-tokens for the letter-type E happen to be practically indistinguishable as to shape, but this is a contingency due to the excellence of the printer's font. It is not necessary that two tokens be indistinguishable, or even similar in shape, in order to be tokens of the same letter-type. An E printed in boldface is quite different from an E in italics, and both differ shapewise from the E-tokens of any penman selected at random. Despite their differences in shape, however, each would be a token of the same letter-type. Thus we return to the problem of specifying what in particular there may be about a given letter-token by virtue of which we associate it with one letter-type rather than with another, or with no letter-type at all.

It has been customary, as we have seen, to approach this problem in terms of the relationship of class membership. As long as we bear in mind that recognition is not a form of classification, this approach is not necessarily misleading. It seems completely natural, in fact, to think of all letter-tokens of a given letter-type as comprising a class of objects, each member of which shares some characteristic with every other member but only with other members of the class. Although we have argued extensively that these characteristics are not to be found among the shape or topological features of the tokens in question, no part of our analysis thus far has suggested that characteristics of this sort cannot be found or that when found they will be incapable of explication. One characteristic of this sort in fact is prima facie obvious. With the class of E-tokens, for example, a characteristic shared in common by all and only members of this class is the characteristic of being used to represent the letter-type E. But the problem of explication remains. We seem unable at the moment, that is, to specify exactly what it is about any particular E-token, or any token of any other letter, by virtue of which it serves to represent its corresponding letter-type. The fact that not all tokens of any given letter-type share common shape characteristics now comes to bear as an indication that representation of a given letter-type does not occur on the basis of shape alone.[4] Indeed, there is no reason to suspect that it should. There is no more reason to think that all tokens of a given letter-type share a common shape than there is to think that all red objects look alike or that all Frenchmen share a common appearance.

Thinking of the problem in terms of classes of letter-tokens and their defining characteristics thus does not in itself lead to a solution. But it helps to underscore certain features of letter-identification, and hence of letter-recognition, which otherwise could remain obscured in the background. First, what we respond to in letter-recognition are letter-tokens. Strictly taken, there is no sense in talking about the recognition of letter-types, since types are not available to sense perception. Second, the characteristics which all tokens of a given letter-type have in common, and in distinction from all other marks, is that they are *used* in a certain way. Each token, that is, serves to repre-

---

[4] It is argued below that the identity of a letter-token depends upon its pattern. Shape and pattern are distinct aspects of an inscription. The *pattern* of an A in Morse code is always a dot followed by a dash. The particular *shapes* of these elements, and hence the shape of the symbol over-all, may be irrelevant to this pattern.

sent the same letter-type as all other tokens in its letter-class. Thus the essential characteristic by which a letter-token is identifiable must be a matter of its use and not a matter of its shape. Third, since a letter-token is a token of its associated type by virtue of its function of representing that type, the recognition of a letter-token must involve doing something in the accomplishment of which this function is disclosed or discharged. If this "something" can be specified, the criterion by which the recognition of a letter-inscription can be distinguished from the mere perception of such an inscription will be at hand. To specify this is the task for the remainder of the present chapter, and for the chapter following.

4. The misconception that a particular mark is a letter-inscription by virtue merely of its shape, or of its topological features, distracts attention from the fact that letter-inscriptions are essentially symbols used by people for communication. That the function of serving communication is essential to a letter has important consequences for our analysis of letter-recognition. It follows from this that a symbol which is not serviceable for communication is not a letter-inscription. And it follows from this in turn that a symbol which no one can *recognize* as a letter-inscription necessarily is *not* a letter-inscription. Let us trace out some of the details of these consequences.

Imagine that a flat stone has been found covered with marks which, although arranged roughly in rows, resemble the characters of no known language. Archaeologists are concerned to determine whether the marks are linguistically significant; only if they are would it be sensible to study them further. The question whether they are linguistically significant is the question whether they served or were intended to serve the purposes of communication. If it could be established that the marks could communicate a message, considerable effort spent in attempting to decipher them would be justified. If, on the other hand, the marks were etched by wind, rain, and frost alone, they would be of no particular archaeological interest. All this is the case without regard to their particular shapes.

This example may be made slightly more fanciful to push the point beyond what is obvious. Suppose that the marks on the stone resemble characters of the Roman alphabet, but that there is room for reasonable doubt that they were inscribed there by anyone who knew that alphabet (radio-carbon tests, let us say, indicate that the marks originated before that alphabet came into use). Now consider the question whether these marks are letter-inscriptions. The question is not whether they have a letter-like shape. By hypothesis their shapes suggest characters of the Roman alphabet. What is in question rather is whether the marks served the purposes of communication. Only if they could be identified as instruments of communication would we be justified in concluding that the marks are letter-inscriptions. If, to the contrary, it could be established that they evince only the "handiwork of nature," it would be at best metaphorical to call them letters at all.

Although this example is fanciful, situations similar to it are rather ordinary. We often find marks on rocks, traces in smooth sand, or grain patterns in wood which have shapes suggestive of characters of the alphabet. But usually there is little inclination to think of these as letter-inscriptions, or as symbols of any other sort. We might say there is a circle on the side of a rock, but we would not say normally that an O had been inscribed there. We might think of a mark in the sand as a loop, but we would not think of it as an E, J, or L.

The point is this: no matter what the shape of a mark may be, it does not count as a letter-inscription unless it is involved somehow in the process of linguistic communication. Now it is obvious that no symbol or mark will serve the purposes of linguistic communication unless it is recognizable in this function by at least some users of some language. But if a mark is recognizable by no language-user (past, present, or future), then it serves no purpose of communication, and hence cannot be counted as a letter-inscription.

The upshot of this is more grave than the examples might lead one to expect. We have been trying to relate the concept of *being* a letter-inscription to the concept of being *recognizable* as a letter-inscription. We noted in the previous chapter that in order for a thing to be recognizable as a certain object, it must in fact be such an object. But the nature of this dependency in the case of letter-inscriptions begins to appear in a different light. It is not, as one might at first assume, that being a letter-inscription is merely a necessary (but not sufficient) condition for being recognizable as a letter-inscription. It is the case, rather, that a given mark *is* a letter-inscription *because* it is recognizable as such. Being recognizable as a letter-inscription is both a necessary *and* a sufficient condition for being a letter-inscription. In this respect, the logic of letter-recognition differs from the logic of the recognition of apples, finches, and familiar faces. An apple is an apple, and a finch a finch, independently of whether anyone may happen to be able to recognize one as such. But marks are not letter-inscriptions independently of being recognizable. Rather, there is a biconditionality between being and being recognizable as a letter-inscription. A letter-inscription *is* any symbol which is recognizable as such. It is as correct to say, in other words, that a symbol is a letter-inscription because of its being so recognized, as it is to say that a symbol is recognized as a letter-inscription because it is one.

This ties in with the fact, by now familiar, that there is

no room for an intelligible contrast between "correct" and "incorrect recognition" of letter-inscriptions. The phrase 'incorrect recognition' could only be presumed to mean something in regard to the recognition of an object as something which in fact it is not. But this is impossible. More particularly, with the case of letter-inscriptions, it is impossible to recognize a symbol as a letter-inscription, when indeed it is not, because necessarily any symbol recognizable as a letter-inscription *is* a letter-inscription. We shall want to say moreover, when the time comes to consider the matter, that one cannot "mistakenly recognize" a particular letter-token as being of a letter-type which in fact it does not represent. The alternative which is meaningful in this connection is that between recognition and no recognition at all; there is no meaningful alternative between "correct" and "incorrect recognition."

This ties in also, retrospectively, with the fact that the concept of recognition cannot be reduced to the concept of correct classification. It would surely be agreed that a mark which is classified as a letter-inscription is classified correctly if, but only if, it *is* a letter-inscription. We have argued that a mark is a letter-inscription if and only if it is recognizable as such. It follows that a mark which is classified as a letter-inscription is *classified correctly* if and only if it is recognizable as a letter-inscription. But it is certainly not the case that a mark which is classified as a letter-inscription is *recognized* as a letter-inscription if and only if it is recognizable as such. There is always the possibility of correct classification which is the result of a guess or of incorrect information, in which case we surely would not count correct classification as an instance of recognition. At any rate, although there may be some conditions under which *correct classification* is biconditionally dependent upon being recognizable, these are not conditions under which being *recognized* is biconditionally dependent upon being *recognizable*. An old conclusion follows on fresh grounds: recognition is not the equivalent of correct classification.[5]

The point of this section may be summed up as follows. To say of a symbol that it is a letter-inscription but that no one can recognize it as a letter-inscription is contradictory; while to say that a symbol which can be *used* as a letter-inscription *is* a letter-inscription is a tautology. The reason this point is worth making is that it provides a new focus for the problem of finding the distinction between the recognition of and the failure to recognize a mark as a letter-inscription. A mark is a letter-inscription if it serves a certain function regarding linguistic communication. The question 'Is this mark a letter-inscription?' thus means, not 'Does this mark have such-and-such a shape?', but rather 'Can so-and-so be done with this mark?'. The task of specifying what this "so-and-so" amounts to, in turn, is a matter of specifying the difference between the behavior, relative to a given mark, of a person who does and that of a person who does not recognize that mark as a letter-inscription. This is the original problem of this chapter, to which we may now turn directly.

5. There is a further distinction between recognition and classification which, although previously passed by, at this point takes on a fundamental importance. This has to do with the fact that recognition involves the ac-

---

[5] This argument may be schematized. We have argued above that (1) x is a letter-inscription if and only if (2) x is recognizable as a letter-inscription. The present argument concerns a symbol x which is classified as a letter-inscription. The argument is that (3) x is *correctly* classified if and only if (1) x *is* a letter-inscription. Hence (3) if and only if (2). But it is not the case (4) that x is *recognized* as a letter-inscription if and only if (2) x is recognizable as a letter-inscription. Hence (3) is not equivalent to (4). It follows that there are circumstances in which to classify an object correctly is not to recognize that object.

quisition of new information, whereas classification involves the exercise of information already at hand.

The term 'information', never univocal, has become even more ambiguous in general discourse with its adoption for a specific use in Information Theory. For the moment, let us retain the term for use in a more general sense, roughly equivalent to 'knowledge'. When one classifies an object, whether an egg, a student, or a mark on a piece of paper, as a rule (excluding "shots in the dark") one applies information about the object gained prior to the act of classification. To classify an egg as marketable requires knowing at least that it is fresh and unfertilized. To classify a student on the C-level is to apply previously acquired information about his ability and performance. In neither case does the classification reveal new information about the thing classified. Similarly, to classify an inscription (as being well-formed, a closed figure, or an A) is to use information about the inscription which is already at hand. To *recognize* a fresh egg, an average student, or a letter-inscription, on the other hand, is not merely to apply previously acquired information, but rather to gain information about the object recognized. Between the moment just before and the moment just after recognition of a fresh egg there is an increase, in some sense, in what is known about the egg by the person who recognizes it. And between a given moment before and a given moment after one's recognition of a letter-inscription, there is an increase in the information one has in regard to that inscription. At least one knows after, what one did not know before, that the inscription is a token of some determinable letter-type.

Critical readers may begin to demur with the notion of letter-recognition as the acquisition of information in the general sense of the term thus far employed. It is unexceptionable to speak of acquiring information through reading a page inscribed with grammatically ordered words and phrases. But can anything important be said about gaining information in this sense through the recognition of letter-inscriptions independently of linguistic context? In fact, to push the question of terminology one step farther, there is something contrived in speaking about the *recognition* of letter-inscriptions in just these terms. The commerce in which intelligent persons normally engage with a series of letter-inscriptions is better described as "reading" than as "recognizing." It would be distinctly odd, while reading a page, to reply to the question 'What are you doing?' by saying merely 'recognizing letter-inscriptions'. There are occasions, it must be admitted, on which this would be a natural answer to the question 'What are you doing?'; one might respond this way, for example, while taking an eye examination. But letter-recognizing situations of this sort differ from the typical reading situation in several ways, the most obvious of which perhaps is that in the former the inscriptions we recognize do not occur in the context of an intelligible message.

Yet there is a sense in which it is quite proper to say we recognize letter-inscriptions while reading a printed or written page. In this sense it would definitely be wrong to say that a person does *not* recognize the letters of a text he is reading. That is, to suggest that a person could read a line of letter-inscriptions most of which he does not recognize would be, not merely odd, but downright false. So there *is* a sense in which one can be said to recognize the individual inscriptions of a text, to which his response as a whole is best called "reading." And insofar as it is proper to speak of the recognition of individual inscriptions in this sense, we might expect that there is a sense also in which this recognition involves the acquisition of information. But 'information' begins to take on a more special meaning. For although we gain information in the sense of 'knowledge' in reading a printed message, surely we do not gain information in exactly the same sense in our response to the individual characters which compose a printed or written message.

There is at least one respect in which it is unquestionable that a person receives information by virtue of his recognition of a letter-inscription, independently of the semantic content of the context in which the inscription occurs. Imagine two persons, O and P, both of whom perceive the sentence 'Theaetetus sits' inscribed on a page, but only the first of whom recognizes the individual letter-inscriptions of which the sentence is composed. The sense in which O recognizes the individual inscriptions is the sense in which it would be false to deny that he recognizes inscriptions of which the sentence which he reads is composed. P cannot recognize the inscriptions in this sense (perhaps he reads only Chinese characters, or is totally illiterate). In recognizing the first letter of the inscribed sentence, O learns at very least that a T-token has been inscribed in this position by the writer of the sentence, whereas it would have been possible for any one of twenty-five different letters to have been inscribed instead. To learn this is to acquire information, in this case information about what the writer of the sentence actually wrote relative to what he might have written in this particular letter-position. P fails to acquire this information; for even if he knew that the alphabet in which the sentence is written contains in all twenty-six different letters, he would not know any more after perceiving the letters than before perceiving them about the choice made by the writer at this juncture.

The essential difference between the responses of O and P to the letter-inscriptions which they perceive is that the former receives information through his perception which the latter fails to perceive. This difference is manifest in the structure of O's behavior subsequent to his recognition, in respects which are absent in P's subsequent behavior. But let us for the moment restrain questions about the significance of acquiring information of this sort. It is sufficient to note that there is a sense of the term 'information' in which it is essential that a person who perceives and recognizes a letter-inscription acquires information through his perception, which a person who perceives but fails to recognize does not acquire.

We may consolidate our gains to this point. Recognition of a letter-inscription is perception of the inscription given the ability to identify it. The ability to identify a given letter-inscription may be conceived as tantamount to the ability to receive information upon perception of that inscription. Perception of the inscription in itself does not constitute recognition, nor does ability to identify the inscription considered independently of some sensory perception of it. But when perception of a letter-inscription concurs with the ability to identify it, this amounts to recognition of the inscription. And the manifestation of this transaction is the acquisition of information through the perception of the inscription.

These remarks provide a framework of a solution to the problem of the criterion of recognition which has been pursued throughout the present chapter. To fill in the details is the task of the next chapter, in which an attempt is made to relate the basic concepts of Information Theory to the concept of letter-recognition.

CHAPTER ELEVEN

THE INFORMATION-
THEORETIC MODEL

1. Let us conceive letter-recognition to be the successful outcome of a communication transaction between (at least) two language users, x who initiates the communication by inscribing a series of letters and y who terminates the transaction by recognizing these inscriptions. It has been suggested (1) that the recognition of a letter-inscription by y amounts to the acquisition of information by y upon his perception of the inscription. This is just what we should expect while thinking of letter-recognition as the termination of a communication transaction; for surely the successful termination of any process of communication between x and y will result in the acquisition of information on the part of y.

When letter-recognition is conceived in this way, other conclusions of the preceding chapter which at first may have seemed adventuresome now begin to appear more matter-of-course. What is essential for communication between x and y, in this way of thinking, is not that the symbols used in communication present a particular predetermined appearance to y, but rather that they convey to y the same information imparted to them by x. Thus, as argued above, (2) letter recognition is not essentially a response to shape characteristics of given letter-inscriptions, and perforce is not a classification of these inscriptions on the basis of such characteristics. Moreover, since letter-recognition is nothing more nor less than the successful outcome of a particular communication transaction involving written language, no symbol which fails to be recognizable as a letter-inscription can serve as a letter-inscription. Thus, as argued above, (3) being recognizable as a letter-inscription is not only a sufficient condition for being a letter-inscription, but a necessary condition as well. To be a letter-inscription is the same as to be recognizable as such. These three points are the major conclusions of the preceding chapter.

If this way of thinking about letter-recognition does not at first seem quite intuitive, partial blame may be due to the fact that the time gap between origination and reception of information is typically longer for communication through written language than for other common means of communication. In fact, although writing in script is only one of several ways in which humans communicate by means of visually perceptible patterns, it has more in common with these other ways than might at first be obvious. The main difference between writing in script and communication by semaphore, for instance, apart from the different symbols employed, is in the amount of time information is stored in the process of being communicated. By the nature of any communication system involving flags (or hand signals, or flashes of light) information normally is received almost at the instant it is sent. In a system of smoke signals, for another example, information is stored very briefly in configurations of smoke clouds; but the time in storage is necessarily very short because of the rapid dispersion of smoke in the atmosphere. By contrast, it is normal that the information imparted in the writing of script remain stored for more or less extended periods of time before the process of communication is completed. The purpose in general of writing in script is to communicate with persons who are not present at the time and place of inscription. When letter symbols are inscribed on a writing surface, the information they represent is stored until the time at which the script is read. If the script is never read, the information it contains is never brought out of storage and the process of communication initiated by the writing is never completed.

These features of writing in script are entirely obvious. The reason for noting them is to point out that the amount of time information remains in storage between the writing and the reading of a series of script characters is inessential to the communication transaction accomplished by the writing and the reading. Assuming that the inscription remains legible, we may ignore the time lapse between the writing and the reading while considering the information-transmission properties of the transaction. What we cannot ignore is that at least two language-users are involved in the transaction. Insofar as we think of the recognition of letter-inscriptions as the completion of the transaction, we must think of this recognition as an achievement which requires the proper performance of at least two persons. As the successful completion of the communication transaction, letter-recognition on the part of one person is a response to something another person does. It is not a response merely to the symbols by means of which in part the other person does this thing. If the symbols do not contain information (consider the "letter" etched on stone by frost and erosion), then no information can be obtained from them when they are perceived; and whether a given set of symbols contains information cannot be determined by observing their shape alone. To characterize the information contained in a series of letter-inscriptions, one must say something about the origin of the inscriptions as well.

This fact has consequences of importance for our thinking about letter-recognition mechanisms. It means that successful letter-recognition, whether human or mechanical, is part of a complex communication transaction which involves a source as well as a receiver of information, and in which the particular symbols used are important only with regard to their function of conveying information from source to receiver. Letter-recognition cannot be properly construed, in particular, merely as the process of classifying, or in some other way characterizing, the shape of the letter-inscriptions themselves.

When y recognizes one or several letters inscribed by x, the state of y's information is altered. His information regarding what x has done is increased. If y fails to recognize, but mistakenly believes he has recognized inscriptions by x, his information in this regard tends to decrease. And if y neither recognizes nor believes he has recognized a given inscription by x, he fails thereby to enter into communication with x relative to this symbol and his information regarding what x has done in this respect remains unaltered. To determine whether or not y has recognized a letter inscribed by x, one must know something about the transaction between x and y.

A precise mathematical model exists for studying this transaction between x and y. Suggestively enough for our purposes, this model is called "Information Theory." Information Theory was developed originally as a tool for understanding aspects of communication systems based on electronic equipment. But during the past few years, an increasing number of applications for Information Theory have been found among the behavioral sciences as well. The thesis of the present chapter is that the basic concepts of Information Theory can be fruitfully applied in connection with the problems which we have seen to be associated with the human behavior of letter-recognition and with its mechanical simulation.

In this application, Information Theory will be deployed as a model and not as a literal description. The model of Information Theory becomes available for our purposes if we are willing to think of the writer and the recognizer of letter-inscriptions respectively as a sender and a receiver of information through a channel of communication consisting of the letter-inscriptions themselves. There will be no occasion to claim that the human function of letter-recognition involves *nothing* but the reception of information, or that human recognizers receive information in a way entirely analogous to radio or television receivers. Yet it seems entirely natural to think of human letter-recognition in terms of this model. Apart from the conceptual advantages of thinking in this way in the context of our present problematic, which we have yet to examine, no further justification of the Information-Theoretic model will be offered.

2. Let us generalize the reference of 'x' and 'y', leaving it open whether x and y are pieces of electronic equipment (for example, radio, radar, television, or telephone units) or, as we have considered them, human beings communicating through written symbols. X and y, together with the channel through which they communicate, will be spoken of collectively as a *communication system*.

It has already been mentioned that the lapse of time between the writing and the reading of script is inessential in any consideration of the information transmitted between x and y as writer and reader. This requirement also will be generalized. The time a message remains in storage as part of the process of transmission from x to y will never be relevant to the informational aspects of the process. Thus the symbols in terms of which x's message is represented for purposes of communication must be capable of representing the message completely unaltered in storage as in transmission. Part of x's function as sender of the message is to formulate it in such symbols, and part of y's function as receiver is to recover the message from the symbolization. The process of formulating information in such symbols will be called "encoding," and the process of recovering the information from the symbols will be called "decoding."

Not all communication requires encoding and decoding in the sense stipulated above. In some contexts, for example, a raised hand is informative without further symbolization. But whatever information is contained in a raised hand can be *stored* only by symbolizing it in some other way (perhaps by photographing the hand in position). The requirement for our purposes that information must be both encoded and decoded as part of the process of communication follows the requirement that information transmitted from x to y must be capable of being stored as part of the process of transmission.

A further requirement of fundamental importance is that each sequence of symbols used for encoding information at the source must be capable of unique decoding by the receiver. This might be called the requirement of *reversibility,* or of *reconstructability.*[1] There must exist rules of coding which insure that each different sequence of the original message is encoded differently from other

---

[1] Khinchin formulates this requirement succinctly: "It goes without saying that the rules of coding must guarantee that the original text can be uniquely reconstructed from the coded text, which requires in particular that different sequences of the uncoded text must be coded differently." *Mathematical Foundations of Information Theory,* by A. I. Khinchin, trans. by R. A. Silverman and M. D. Friedman (New York, Dover Publications, Inc., 1957), p. 23.

sequences, and rules of decoding which insure that the
original message thus encoded can be recovered without
loss or alteration of content. The existence of such rules,
of course, does not guarantee that no mistake will be made
in the transmission of information from source to receiver.
The rules must guarantee rather that the structure of the
message is not altered in transmission because of ambiguity or insufficient articulation in the system of symbols
used for encoding. It should be apparent, in this connection, that y has received the full extent of the information
transmitted by x only if y is capable of reproducing the
information in a form which bears a one-to-one correspondence to the form of the original. It is not necessary,
however, that the information be expressed in exactly the
same format before and after transmission. Thus the ordinary Roman alphabet provides a system of symbolization
by which a message originally expressed in spoken English can be completely reproduced in script or in print.

The term 'information' as used thus far in this chapter
clearly has nothing directly to do with meaning, or the
semantic content of language. In fact, as far as the information-transmission characteristics of a communication system are concerned, it is irrelevant even whether the information transmitted adds up to an intelligible message.
If the letter sequence PBRU, for example, were transmitted to y, the reception of this sequence would yield no
information in the sense of knowledge about extra-linguis-
tic subject matter. But the sequence would yield quite
definite information in the more limited sense of the term
'information' introduced at the end of the preceding
chapter. Y would be informed, in particular, that out of
twenty-six possible letters the letter P had been selected as
first of the series to be transmitted, the letter B as second
of the series, etc. Insofar as it is helpful to think of this
information as being "about" anything at all, it is about

what actually was encoded at the source relative to what might have been encoded alternatively. This is information of a fundamental sort. For despite the fact that such information may have no semantic content, some information of this sort must be communicated as a necessary condition for the communication of information of any other sort whatsoever. If a communication system could not transmit specific sequences of symbols in an unambiguous, reproducible way, it would for that reason be incapable of reliably transmitting messages with semantic significance. It is with the communication of information in this nonsemantic but fundamentally important sense that Information Theory is primarily concerned.

In particular, Information Theory provides a precise numerical measure for the amount of information conveyed from sender to receiver in a given sequence of symbols. This measure can be deployed to provide a description of the information-transmission capabilities in general of a communication system.

Let us begin with the simplest possible example of a communication system. Suppose that the sender can transmit only representations of *yes* and *no* over the communication channel, and that there is an equal probability of transmitting either message. Assume further that each symbol is faithfully received and that the receiver invariably interprets each symbol correctly as either *yes* or *no*. Transmission of the symbol for *yes* will communicate a specific amount of information. Before transmission, the probability of sending *yes* is 50 per cent. After transmission the probability is 100 per cent. Under the assumption of correct reception and interpretation, the receiver's information about whether the sender is to transmit *yes* increases from a 50–50 probability to a 100 per cent certainty with his reception of the message. Since transmission of *no* is equally probable a priori, the receiver's information regarding the transmission of *no* is increased by the same amount when the symbol for *no* is actually received. Since the sender has only two alternatives from which to choose, his actual choice in any case can be represented by one binary digit.[2] For this reason it has become customary to refer to the amount of information conveyed by the choice of one of two equally probable alternatives as a *bit* (*bi*nary dig*it*) of information.

Choice of one alternative out of two which are not of equal probability, however, will not yield exactly one bit of information. In general, the number of bits conveyed by one choice varies with a priori probability in a given context that the alternative actually chosen will in fact be chosen. This probability in turn varies both with the number of possible choices and with the distribution of probabilities within the range of possible alternatives. To illustrate the former source of variability, consider a system in which there are four different possible choices for the sender, each with the same probability of selection. Now it is clear that the actual choice of one of these four equally probable states provides more information than a choice between two equally probable states. Each state of the four is initially only 25 per cent probable, compared with 50 per cent probability of each of the two alternatives, and the increase from 25 per cent to 100 per cent probability involves more information than the increase from 50 per cent to 100 per cent. More *uncertainty* about the

---

[2] The decimal system is named with regard to the fact that all numbers expressed within it are composed of 10 digits, 0 through 9. Ten different alternatives can be represented by one decimal digit. The binary system provides for the expression of all numbers in terms of only two digits, 0 and 1. Just as 10^2 different numbers can be expressed by 2 decimal digits, 2^2 different numbers can be expressed by 2 binary digits. In general, 2^n different items can be uniquely represented by n different binary digits. The first eight numbers of the decimal system, for example, can be expressed by three binary digits, as follows: 000, 001, 010, 011, 100, 101, 110, 111.

state to be chosen is removed by choice of the less probable state. To look at it in another way, more possibilities are *excluded* by choice of one out of four than by choice of one out of two equally probable alternatives. Subsequent to learning about the choice of one out of four, a person knows more about what is *not* the case, which knowledge in turn requires more information for its transmission.

Whereas the choice of one state out of two equally probable states, by definition, conveys one bit of information, it can be seen that the choice of one state out of four equally probable states conveys exactly two bits. To see this, consider that the four states are divided into two pairs of two states each. The choice of a member of either pair is 50 per cent probable. An indication that the one state of the four actually chosen is in a particular one of these two pairs consequently conveys one bit of information. To indicate further which of the two members of this pair is the state chosen conveys one further bit of information. In line with the intuitive requirements that the information conveyed by a number of independent choices shall be additive, selection of this one state out of two pairs of equally probable alternatives can be seen to yield exactly two bits of information.

We may note that the probability of selecting one of two equally probable states is doubled in being changed from 50 per cent to 100 per cent by actual selection of that state, and the probability that one of four equally probable states is doubled *twice* by the actual selection of that state. This corresponds to the number of bits conveyed respectively by the selection of these two states. In doubling the probability of the first state *one* time over, one bit of information is conveyed. In doubling the probability of the other state *two* times over, two bits of information are conveyed. Since a bit of information results from the choice of one of two equally probable alternatives, and since choice of one of two equally probable alternatives is the same as doubling the probability of the alternative chosen, we may conclude that one bit of information is the amount resulting from a specification which doubles the probability of a given state.

The amount of information conveyed by selection of a state of given initial probability thus may be measured in bits by the number of times the initial probability of that state must be doubled to reach 100 per cent. For any given initial probability P_i of state i, the information conveyed by its selection is equal to the number of times P_i must be doubled to equal unity. Let us designate this amount of information by 'I'. The value of I, for any P_i, can be calculated according to the formula:[3]

$$I = -\log_2 P_i$$

This formula provides the basic measure of information upon which other calculations in Information Theory are based. Let us gain familiarity with this equation through

---

[3] In the system of logarithms to the base 10, the number of times a given number is to be multiplied by 10 to produce a quantity equal to a second number is the difference between the logarithms of the two numbers. Thus, 8 twice multiplied by 10 is 800, and the difference between the logarithm of 8 (.90309) and that of 800 (2.90309) is 2. Similarly, in the systems of logarithms to the base 2, the number of times a given number x is to be doubled to produce a product equal to another number y is the number of units difference between the logarithm of x and the logarithm of y. For example, 2 doubled twice equals 8, and the difference between the logarithm of 2 (1.0) and that of 8 (3.0) is 2. Now the logarithm to the base 2 of unity is 0, while the logarithm of any given P_1 is less than 0. The number of times P_1 must be doubled to equal unity thus is given by the expression $0 - \log_2 P_1$. This is the number of the bits of information conveyed by the choice of P_1, justifying the equation $I = -\log_2 P_1$. Other informal derivations of this equation can be found in R. D. Luce's "The Theory of Selective Information and Some of Its Behavioral Applications," *Developments in Mathematical Psychology*, ed. R. D. Luce (The Free Press of Glencoe, Illinois), 1960. Formal derivations can be found in Luce, *ibid.*; in *The Mathematical Theory of Communication*, by C. E. Shannon and W. Weaver (Urbana, The University of Illinois Press, 1949); in *Probability and Information Theory, with Applications to Radar*, by P. M. Woodward (London, Pergamon Press, Ltd., 1953); and elsewhere.

a few applications. Choice of one of five equally probable states conveys $-\log_2 0.20$, or 2.32 bits of information. Choice of a state with probability 0.07 conveys 3.84 bits; of a state with a probability of 0.55, 0.86 bits; etc. Consecutive choice of states with 0.25 and 0.5 probabilities, which itself is 0.25×0.5 probable, conveys 2 plus 1, or 3 bits of information, since logarithms are additive under multiplication of their antilogarithms.

It is obvious that application of this formula is not limited to choices among equally probable states. The formula can be applied to calculate the information content of the choice of any state of which the prior probability of choice is known. Thus, if a choice were to be made among three states, the probabilities of choice of which are 0.10, 0.30, and 0.60, independent choice of each of these states in turn would yield respectively 3.32, 1.74, and 0.74 bits of information. In fact, given the probability of any one of n different choices, we could calculate the information conveyed by the choice of that state without regard to the number of other possible choices or their prior probabilities in particular. Choice of a state which has P_i probability of being chosen conveys $-\log_2 P_i$ bits of information, whether there is a wide range of alternatives or only one other possible choice.

Calculation of the information content of individual choices, however, is seldom of any practical or theoretical interest. Even communication systems designed for special purposes must be capable of transmitting effectively information regarding choices made among a large variety of possible alternatives. A more useful measure of information content can be provided in terms of the average information conveyed per choice among n possible choices of known probability. Choices of low probability convey more information individually, but because of their low frequency of occurrence will account for less information over-all than choices of higher probability. This fact is accounted for in the formula

$$H = \sum_{i=1}^{n} - P_i \log_2 P_i$$

where P_i is the prior probability of choice of the ith state, and H the average information conveyed by choice of one from among the n possible states. To calculate H for a given set of n possible states, one need only calculate $P_i \log_2 P_i$ for each i of the n and add the results, as indicated by the summation sign in the expression of H above.

Something can be seen of the properties of this function by returning to the example in which choice is limited to two alternatives, *yes* and *no*. It is assumed that the probability of choosing one or the other of these two alternatives is unity. If the probability of choosing *yes* is P_i, then the probability of choosing *no* is $1 - P_i$. It can readily be seen by some easy calculations that H is 0.47 when one of the two choices is 10 per cent, 0.72 when one is 20 per cent, etc. The maximum value of H = 1.0 occurs when the two possible choices are of equal probability. This value, of course, is a direct consequence of the definition of the bit as a unit of information, but the reasoning above may help in understanding why one bit is the maximum amount of information per choice that can possibly be conveyed by a communication system admitting choice among only two alternatives at the source.

It is interesting to relate H, the average information content of a message conveyed through a given channel, to what might be called its "channel capacity." The capacity of a given communication channel to convey, or to store, information depends upon the number of alternatives that can be unambiguously represented within that channel in a given time. If there are only two distinguishable states of the channel in terms of which it can represent a message in any given time, then at most one bit of information can be represented in the channel within this time period. If there are four distinguishable states of the channel then, as we have seen, at most two bits of information could be conveyed at a time. This possibility would be realized, of course, only when the alternatives represented by each of the four states were equally likely to occur. In general, the channel capacity of a given communication system may be defined as the logarithm to the base two of the number of distinct alternatives which the channel can represent unambiguously in a given time period. Now some elementary calculations in terms of logarithms of the expression for H will show that when there are n equally probable states among which choice might be made, then choice of one state of the n conveys $\log_2 n$ bits of information. In other words, the channel capacity of a system is employed to the maximum when all of its possible states are equally likely to be chosen at the source. If there are n possible states representable within the channel, and if each message sent over the channel is articulated in terms of choices among n equally probable alternatives, then the channel is being used as efficiently as possible. If, on the other hand, there are n possible choices which are not equally probable, or if there are fewer than n possible choices at the source, then a channel with capacity of $\log_2 n$ bits is not used to its fullest capacity.

It should be obvious at this point that a channel with a capacity of less than $\log_2 n$ bits might be adequate in theory for the transmission of a message in terms of choices among n alternative states if these n states are not equally likely to be chosen. An illustration of this may be provided with reference to the set of twenty-six possible choices provided by the Roman alphabet. The maximum information which could be conveyed by choice of a single alternative among twenty-six is $\log_2 26$, or approximately 4.7 bits. It is well known, however, that the twenty-six letters occur with widely differing frequencies in any intelligible text. Calculation of the average information content per letter on the basis of a standard frequency chart for the English language shows that individual letters convey approximately 4.14 bits of information.[4] This amount is somewhat less than the capacity of a channel of eighteen distinguishable states ($\log_2 18 = 4.17$). Thus the amount of information conveyed by individual letters of our alphabet, when used to express the English language, could in theory be conveyed by an "alphabet" with only eighteen letters. These remarks, it should be noted, do not take into account the fact that the amount of information per letter in actual use is even less than 4.14 because of the tendency of letters to fall within patterns which are more or less predictable. The letter Q, for example, is almost always followed by the letter U in English, and almost never by the letter T. This decreases the information conveyed by the letter Q to an amount below what would be calculated as the information content of Q under the assumption of complete independence among letters in actual use.

One more consequence of these calculations regarding the twenty-six-letter alphabet should be noted. The amount of information contained in the choice of one letter among twenty-six, whatever this may turn out to be in a particular case, can be conveyed as well in any channel which admits at least two distinguishable states. If, for example, the information content of a letter is 3 bits, it would obviously be possible to convey this information in a channel admitting eight different states. But it could be conveyed in terms of only two states also, as long as it

---

4 All calculations in this book are based on the frequency charts in Fletcher Pratt's *Secret and Urgent* (Garden City, N.Y., Blue Ribbon Books, 1939).

is possible to expend three separate choices in the representation of the letter. In general, the number of separate choices required to convey a message of m bits in a system admitting n possibilities is $m/\log_2 n$, rounded to the next largest whole number.

We have discussed only the barest outlines of Information Theory as it concerns communications engineers. Nothing has been said thus far about the ways information can be lost within a system, about the calculation of information content of series of choices which are not independent, about modifications of the basic equations which make possible calculations regarding messages which are not expressed in terms of discrete states, or about a number of special theorems which have been of great importance recently in engineering applications of Information Theory. Although certain of these topics will be discussed below, it should be emphasized again that no attempt has been made here to provide a discussion of Information Theory which is adequate for any purposes other than our own, or which is complete in any technical sense.

There is, however, one more basic concept which should be mentioned in order to make the transition from this to more technical discussions of Information Theory manageable. The expression for H developed above in a very informal fashion was first developed formally in a paper by Shannon published in 1948, in which he noted the identity in form between this expression and the formulation of entropy in statistical mechanics. Thus guided, Shannon called H the *entropy* of the set of probabilities P_i in terms of which it is defined. This has led several authors to speak of the information conveyed by a message as its entropy.[5] Other authors, however, have conceived the rela-

[5] See, for example, C. E. Shannon in *The Mathematical Theory of Communication*, by Shannon and Weaver, p. 20; and L. D. Harmon in *Information Theory*, ed. Colin Cherry (London, Butterworth and Co., Ltd., 1961), p. 306.

tionship between H and entropy in a way which leads them to speak of entropy as the lack of information.[6] The proper way of conceiving the relationship between the measure of average information in Information Theory and entropy in Physics is a matter under debate at the present, and there is no justification for going further into the matter in the present context.[7] It is better instead to adopt the expedient of avoiding the term 'entropy'.

3. The concept of noise in Information Theory makes possible a precise distinction between a successful and an unsuccessful communication transaction. This parallels the distinction drawn in the preceding chapter between recognizing, and perceiving but failing to recognize, a given letter-inscription. It is time to return to the problem of the preceding chapter, with the attempt to characterize the latter distinction in terms of the Information-Theoretic model.

The information represented at the source of a communication system is not always equivalent to what is represented to the receiver. The sender is not invariably successful in getting his message through to the receiver without alteration or loss of content. In an electronic communications system this effect may be due to numerous factors, including errors in coding or in decoding, inadequate information-transmission characteristics of the channel, or static introduced into the system during the process of transmission. These factors may be grouped together under the title 'noise'; their common characteristic

---

[6] *Experimental Music,* by Lejaren Hiller and Leonard Isaacson (New York, McGraw-Hill Book Company, Inc., 1959), p. 26. Reprinted in part in *The Modeling of Mind,* eds. Kenneth Sayre and Frederick Crosson (Notre Dame, University of Notre Dame Press, 1963).

[7] An illuminating nontechnical discussion of the problem may be found in J. R. Pierce, *Symbols, Signals and Noise: The Nature and Process of Communication* (New York, Harper and Brothers, 1961), chap. 10.

is that they represent the introduction of probable error into the communication transaction.

Comparable factors are often present in the communication process which culminates in the recognition of letter-inscriptions by a knowledgeable human being. There can be mistakes in encoding (writing), deficiencies in transmission (blurred, faded, or smudged inscriptions), or mistakes in decoding (reading). The result of any such mistake is a misrepresentation to the reader of the information the writer intended to convey. Unless this misrepresentation is compensated in some way (such as redundancy in the message), the reader will fail to identify the concerned letter-inscription. This means that the information purportedly represented to the reader fails to be identical with the information imparted by the writer.

Let us describe the effects of noise upon communication in terms of the Information-Theoretic model. Prior to the reception of the first symbol in a message sequence, let us assume, y has no information which would indicate the nature of the message originated by x. But since it is known that the symbol sequences transmitted by x will represent intelligible English sentences, y can form an a priori estimation of the likelihood of first receiving any given letter, with reference to a reliable letter-frequency chart for the English language.[8] After reception of the first symbol, the a priori probabilities regarding the identity of following symbols in the sequence is affected by two additional factors. First is the interaction among the probabilities of occurrence of symbols within a common context which we call "redundancy." Thus, for example, transmission of the letter U after the letter Q would convey considerably less information than would transmission of the letter U as the first letter of a sequence. The second factor is the effect upon the probability of occurrence of other inscriptions

---

8 See fn. 4, p. 236.

of a given letter resulting from the response of the receiver
to one particular inscription of that letter. If y correctly
identifies a particular inscription conveyed to him sym-
bolically by x, then information is transmitted from x to
y. If y's response adds up to a mistaken identification of
the inscription, there is a sense in which information is
lost in transmission. In either case (under general conditions to be mentioned below) the information transaction
between x and y involves changes in the estimated probabilities of occurrence of that letter which are independent
of considerations of redundancy. It is with regard to this
second factor that the effect of noise upon information
transmission can be most profitably described for our
purposes.

To understand how this factor operates, let us return to
the highly simplified illustration in which choice of state
to be transmitted is limited to two alternatives, *no* and *yes*.
In order to distinguish between states transmitted and
states received, however, the latter will be designated *stop*
and *go*. *No* and *yes* correspond respectively to *stop* and *go*,
so that the choice of *no* at the source will correctly be
transmitted if *stop* is indicated to the receiver, but incorrectly transmitted if *go* is indicated, and so forth. Let us
assume that the a priori probability of *yes* being chosen at
the source is known by both sender and receiver. This
means, for the present illustration, that the proportion of
choices of *yes* and the proportion of choices of *no* in a
representative sample of choices can be expressed by two
specific fractions, the sum of which is unity. Now it can
be shown by elementary calculations that the amount of
information in bits conveyed by each choice of *yes* in this
situation, given noise-free transmission, is equal to the
logarithm to the base two of the reciprocal of the fraction
of such choices. But this is obviously the case only if no
error enters into the transmission of these choices; for it
is clear that less information will be conveyed to y by a

given choice on the part of x if y incorrectly interprets the symbol expressing the choice than if y's interpretation were correct.

It is unrealistic, in considering any actual communication system, to assume that all choices of the sender will be correctly identified by the receiver. Let us construct our simplified system accordingly to provide for a certain proportion of *yes*'s the representations of which are interpreted as *stop* by the receiver and a certain proportion of *no*'s yielding interpretations of *go*. Consider that the over-all proportion of *yes* among all choices by x is 5/7, that the over-all proportion of *go*'s among all indications to y is 4/7, and that the over-all probability of a *yes*-choice resulting in a *go*-indication is 60 per cent, over a given range of choices. These quantities, and other relevant quantities entailed by them, can be represented as in Table 1, where each choice represents 1/7 of all choices under consideration.

v	yes	yes	yes	yes	yes	no	no
w	go	go	go	stop	stop	stop	go

v		yes	yes	no	no
w		go	stop	go	stop
$P(v, w)$		$\frac{3}{7}$	$\frac{2}{7}$	$\frac{1}{7}$	$\frac{1}{7}$
$P(v)$		$\frac{5}{7}$	$\frac{5}{7}$	$\frac{2}{7}$	$\frac{2}{7}$
$P(w)$		$\frac{4}{7}$	$\frac{3}{7}$	$\frac{4}{7}$	$\frac{3}{7}$
$P_w(v)$		$\frac{3}{4}$	$\frac{2}{3}$	$\frac{1}{4}$	$\frac{1}{3}$
$P_v(w)$		$\frac{3}{5}$	$\frac{2}{5}$	$\frac{1}{2}$	$\frac{1}{2}$
$I_{v, w}$		.070	−.100	−.193	.222

Table 1

In this table, the probability that x will choose a given state v (either *no* or *yes*) is designated 'P(v)', and the probability that w (either *stop* or *go*) will be indicated to y is designated 'P(w)'. Examination of the chart at the head of the table will show that *yes* is paired with *go* in 3/7 of all combinations of v and w, that *yes* is paired with *stop* in 2/7 of all combinations, and that *no* is paired with *go* and with *stop* each in 1/7 of all combinations. These proportions are designated 'P(v,w)'. The designations '$P_w(v)$', '$P_v(w)$' and '$I_{v,w}$' remain to be explained.

Now it is apparent from the chart that the a priori probability of choosing *yes* is different from the probability that *yes* has been chosen after *go* is indicated to y. Prior to any choice, the probability that *yes* will be chosen, when x has occasion to choose between *yes* and *no*, is 5/7. But after *go* has been indicated to y, the probability that *yes* was chosen, as y can best estimate, is instead 3/4. This figure merely expresses the fact that three out of four *go*-indications originate in our sample with a choice of *yes*. The probability that *yes* has been chosen, given an indication of *go*, may be thought of as the *conditional probability* of *yes*, given *go*. In general, the conditional probability that v has been chosen, given w, is designated '$P_w(v)$'. In a similar fashion, the probability that w will be indicated when v is chosen will differ from the a priori probability that w will be indicated. The conditional probability that w will be indicated, given v, is designated '$P_v(w)$'.

It is a matter of common sense that more information will be conveyed to y when he interprets x's signal correctly than when his interpretation is incorrect. A precise measure is available for this difference in information conveyed by correct and by incorrect indications to y. The rationale behind this measure may be developed in terms of an example.

Before *yes* is chosen by x, the probability of choosing *yes* is 5/7. It is assumed that y is aware of this probability.

Now if the choice of *yes* were invariably accompanied by an indication of *go* to y, the probability of having chosen *yes* when *go* is indicated would be unity. Accordingly, in this noise-free case, y would receive $-\log_2 P(v)$ bits of information, when 'P(v)' indicates the a priori probability (5/7) of a *yes*-choice. But choice of *yes* does not always result in an indication of *go* in our example. Instead, the probability of having chosen *yes*, given an indication of *go*, is only 3/4. The information conveyed to y by an indication of *go*, consequently, is measured according to the change of probability from 5/7 to 3/4. In effect, y has failed to receive the information that would be conveyed with a change of probability from 3/4 to unity. The amount of information y actually receives is the difference between what he would have received if the probability had changed from 5/7 to unity and what he would have received if the probability had changed from 3/4 to unity. In a word, the latter amount is the difference between what he would have received under noise-free conditions and what he actually received given the fact that only 3/4 of the *go*'s received are reliable indications of *yes*.

Just as the information received by y under noise-free conditions is $-\log_2 P(v)$, the amount of this information he failed to receive is $-\log_2 P_w(v)$. The amount of information actually conveyed to y by an indication of *go* is the difference between these amounts, or

$$-\log_2 P(v) - (-\log_2 P_w(v)) = \log_2 \frac{P_w(v)}{P(v)} .$$

This expression provides a quantitative measure of the amount of information conveyed from x to y when v is chosen by x under conditions where probability of choice of v is $P(v)$, and when w is indicated to y under conditions where probability of indication of v given w is $P_w(v)$.

Designating this quantity of information conveyed from x to y by '$I_{v,w}$', we have finally

$$I_{v,w} = \log_2 \frac{P_w(v)}{P(v)} \cdot$$

This equation can be applied to show a fundamental difference between the results of a correct identification of a transmitted symbol and the results of an incorrect identification.

Examination of Table 1 will show that the value attached to $I_{v,w}$, under the conditions of our extremely simplified illustration, will always be greater than zero if w is a correct indication of v, and will always be less than zero if w is an incorrect indication of v. Whenever $P_w(v)$ is greater than $P(v)$, the information conveyed by reception of w will be positive in amount, and whenever $P_w(v)$ is less than $P(v)$ the information will be negative. In the former case, a positive amount of information has been conveyed by the reception of w. In the latter case, we may say that a "negative amount" has been conveyed. In the case of the third possibility, when $P_w(v)$ is equal to $P(v)$, then v and w are statistically independent, and no information is conveyed regarding v by the reception of w.

In general, whenever the probability of choosing a certain value of v is increased by the reception of a given value of w, information relative to v is gained by the reception of that w; and whenever the likelihood of choice of a certain v is decreased by reception of a value of w, information relative to v is lost by reception of that w. This is the case regardless of the number of possible values admitted by either v or w. In the context of our particular example, it is apparent that $P_w(v)$ represents an increase over $P(v)$ whenever w is the correct indication of v, and represents a decrease from $P(v)$ whenever w is an incorrect indication of v. This is the case in general, provided that the probability that w will give a correct indication of a given value of v is greater than all probabilities that w will give an incorrect indication.[9]

These remarks may be summarized. It is a matter of definition that y's information in regard to a possible choice by x is increased whenever there is an increase in the probability of that choice as determined by y. The maximum amount of information is conveyed to y by a given choice when the probability of that choice can be correctly determined by y to be unity. This maximum is not attained when there is some probability that y might misinterpret the signal representing x's choice. But even in communication systems where such a probability exists,[10] which of course is the typical condition of most if not all actual communication systems, a correct identification by y of x's representation of a choice will result in an increase in the probability that x has actually made the choice associated with that representation.

Thus a correct identification of a signal received by y (in any plausible communication system) will always re-

---

[9] A positive amount of information will always be conveyed by correct identification of a signal w_k as indicating a choice v_k, in any communication system admitting n discrete states, provided that, for all k

$$P_{w_k}(v_k) > \sum_{j=1}^{n} P_{w_j}(v_k) P_{w_j} \quad ;$$

and a negative amount of information will always be conveyed by an incorrect identification in the same terms, provided that, when $i \neq k$

$$P_{w_k}(v_i) < \sum_{j=1}^{n} P_{w_j}(v_i) P_{w_j} \quad .$$

These conditions are certainly met at least by any operable system for the transmission of information employing the Roman alphabet as a channel of communication. (I am indebted to Dr. James Massey of the University of Notre Dame for the formulation of these conditions, and for helpful advice on various technical aspects of the discussion in this chapter.)

[10] This remark is subject to the condition formalized in fn. 9.

sult in the communication of a positive amount of information to y. An incorrect identification of a signal by y, on the other hand, will always result in a negative amount of information communicated to y. The invariable distinction between the correct and the incorrect identification of an information-bearing symbol, in any interesting communication system, is that a positive amount of information is conveyed by a correct identification and a negative amount of information is conveyed by an incorrect identification.

4. These properties of $I_{v,w}$ apply directly to the problem of Chapter Ten—the problem of finding a distinguishing mark between recognition and the failure to recognize a given letter-inscription. Let us translate what has been said regarding these properties into the language of letter-recognition. The channel of communication now is a surface inscribed with letter-tokens of the alphabet. The source of signals over the channel, designated 'x' above, is the penman who inscribes the surface. And the receiver of the message, designated 'y' above, is the person who reads or attempts to read the inscribed surface. When y correctly interprets a letter-inscription, we say he recognizes it (in the sense of the term discussed above according to which it would be false to say a person can read a text composed of characters he cannot recognize). When y fails to interpret an inscription correctly upon perceiving it, we say he has failed to recognize it. To interpret a letter-inscription correctly is to take a given signal in the channel as representing the same choice out of a specific number of alternatives (in this case twenty-six) that the writer intended it to represent. To interpret an inscription incorrectly is to take the inscription as representing a different choice from that the writer intended. In the former case, the probability of the choice which x actually made,

as it can be estimated from the point of view of y, is greater after than before the interpretation, and y consequently has gained information in his perception of the inscription. In the latter case, the probability of the choice actually made is decreased by y's interpretation, and the result is loss of information.

In sum, for y to recognize a given letter-inscription is for y to perceive that inscription and to gain information through his perception. Failure to recognize a given letter-inscription, on the other hand, can mean one of two things: either no interpretation whatsoever is ventured, or an incorrect interpretation is made. In the former case, no information exchange takes place between x and y: y is neither more nor less knowledgeable regarding the choice among the twenty-six letters of the alphabet which that inscription represents. In the latter case, there is an information loss on the part of y as a result of his perception of the inscription.

Thus the difference between recognizing a given letter-inscription, and perceiving but failing to recognize that inscription, is that with the former but not with the latter there is a gain in information on the part of the perceiver. This, of course, is where we were left at the end of the preceding chapter. But now we are able to fill in the details.

A gain in information is equivalent to a decrease in uncertainty regarding the identity of a choice made at the source of information. Thus, to gain information through the perception of a letter-inscription is to become less uncertain about the letter which the writer intended to indicate in making his inscription. This uncertainty is measured in terms of the probability that a given letter be chosen before and after actual choice of the letter. Choice of an initially improbable letter like Q or Z, accordingly, results in a change from a low probability to a high one, and hence has the potential of communicating a relatively large amount of information; choice of a more probable letter like E or T, on the other hand, removes less uncertainty and hence is capable only of communicating less information. Correct identification of a given inscription constitutes the completion of the communication transaction, with the resulting increase in information on the part of the perceiver making the identification. Mistaken identification, instead of decreasing uncertainty in regard to the choice of the writer, actually increases uncertainty. The change of uncertainty in either case can be precisely measured in terms of the probabilities of choice from the point of view of the perceiver before and after his perception of the inscription.

It has been emphasized that acceptance of the Information-Theoretic model as a conceptual framework in which letter-recognition can be profitably discussed does not commit one to construing the model as a literal description of what actually takes place in human letter-recognition. Nonetheless, the remarks above concerning what transpires in the process of communicating through script (with one exception to be discussed in the following chapter) seem entirely in accord with our ordinary conception of what happens when a person recognizes a letter-inscription.

It might be objected at this point that our explication of letter-recognition in terms of the acquisition of information provides at best a very elusive solution to the problem of criterion posed in the preceding chapter. The problem was there construed as one of specifying what in particular marks the difference between the behavior of the person who recognizes and the behavior of the person who perceives but fails to recognize a given letter-inscription. It was laid down as a condition for any solution of the problem that this difference, whatever in the end it may amount to, must in some way be manifest in observable behavior. The difficulty with explicating this difference in terms of the acquisition of information, it may appear, is that the acquisition of information often is not a matter of observable behavior at all.

Now it is clear enough that we should not *expect* the acquisition of information itself to be observable. To receive information is a mental act, and mental acts just aren't open to observation in any straightforward sense. Similarly, recognition itself, also being a mental act, is not open to observation. Were this not the case, the problem of criterion would not have arisen in the first place. So there is no call to be disturbed by the fact that neither recognition on the one hand, nor the acquisition of information on the other, are in themselves observable aspects of behavior. But at the same time it must be admitted that little advance has been made on the problem of simulating letter-recognition if our analysis to this point has resulted merely in refocusing the problem from one unobservable act to another. Our present situation, however, is not so unfortunate. Returning to the model of Information Theory, we find reason to suspect that the acquisition of information through the recognition of letter-inscriptions is accompanied by an ability the exercise of which is in the fullest sense observable.

The successful completion of the communication transaction in our model, involving as it does both the encoding and the decoding of a message, is the acquisition of information through the reception and successful decoding of that message. Now it was stipulated that information will be considered to have been successfully conveyed from a source to a receiver only if the receiver is able to reconstruct the message in the same form as the original, or in a form which is structurally equivalent to the original. Reconstruction of the original message is not the same as decoding the received signal. Thus a telegrapher is able to decode an incoming series of dots and dashes without reacting in any observable way to the message, in particular without typing or writing the message in a form corresponding to its original English expression. But normally he *will* transpose the received signal back into the natural language of the original message. And in cases where he does not do this, we would say he must be *able* to do it, given the ability to type or to write, if it is to be admitted that he has in fact received the message correctly. In a word, although the reception of information is not the same as the reconstruction of the original message, we want to say that information has been received only if the receiver is *able* to reconstruct the original message in this way.

It seems clear that this is what we want to say also in regard to the recognition of letter-inscriptions by a human perceiver. A person who claims to recognize a given inscription, but is unable (not merely unwilling) to transpose the symbol which he received into an equivalent form, would be considered not really to have recognized the inscription. It is enough that he is able to write the symbol himself in an acceptable form, or that he be able to articulate its phonetic equivalent. But if he can do nothing of this sort, he simply doesn't get the message. This further application of the Information-Theoretic model also seems to be intuitively correct: insofar as the recognition of a letter-inscription is conceived as the acquisition of information upon perception of the inscription, a necessary condition of recognition is that the perceiver be able to repeat the inscription or to reconstruct its content in equivalent form.

The mark of letter-recognition thus turns out to be the presence of an ability. One does not *always* manifest the ability to reconstruct a letter-inscription upon recognizing it; but unless one *does* make this ability manifest upon the occurrence of some one of a variety of appropriate occasions which are easy to specify, he does not in fact recognize the inscription.

We have returned along a very different route to the previous contention, made on the basis of an analysis of recognition in general, that letter-recognition is perception of a letter-symbol given a certain ability on the part of the perceiver. The previous analysis resulted in the claim of equivalence between (i) recognition and (ii) perception given the ability to identify. Application of the model of Information Theory has led to the assertion of equivalence between (i) recognition of a given letter-inscription and (iii) the perception of that inscription given the ability to reproduce it. A further indication of the appropriateness of the Information-Theoretic model is the intuitive congruence between (ii) being able to identify and (iii) being able to reproduce a given inscription. Although there undoubtedly are things one can identify without being able to reproduce in a relevant sense, and probably some things one can reproduce without being able to identify, it appears that the two abilities converge entirely with regard to letter-inscriptions. If a person can identify a letter-inscription correctly, we have argued, he must be able to reproduce it, whether phonetically, in script, or in some other representation. And it seems to be the case, on the other hand, that reproducing a letter-inscription in one of these ways is just what we would expect a person to do if we asked him to identify the inscription. Since neither the ability to identify nor the ability to reproduce given letter-inscription apparently can occur without the other, we may treat them as equivalent for our purposes.

5. One further moral of immediate interest may be drawn from the Information-Theoretic model. Recognition of a given letter-inscription is perception of the

inscription resulting in the acquisition of information. Recognition is absent, of course, when there is no perception of the inscription, or when the inscription is perceived in the absence of an increase of information on the part of the perceiver. Now there are various influences within a mechanical communication system which might result in information loss or in a transaction involving no information exchange at all. The machine at the receiving end of the communication channel might make a mistake in decoding, or might simply fail to respond to an incoming signal. But it is possible for an attempt to communicate to be thwarted as well by faulty encoding, or by a muddling of the signal as it is conveyed through the channel. In an electronic communication system, viewed within the context of Information Theory, these effects are conceived as noise.

Corresponding disruptive influences operate in the human transaction culminating in the recognition of letter-inscriptions. Absence of recognition might be the result, of course, of an improper or inadequate performance on the part of the potential recognizer. But it might result also from poor writing, or from a blurred or faded inscription which is the fault of neither the writer nor the reader. In order for person y to recognize an inscription made by x, there are things which y must do correctly. But there are also things which x must do correctly, and things which must occur in a proper fashion in connection with the passage of the inscription from x to y.

Obvious as these facts may be, they are thoroughly obscured when one attempts to think of letter-*recognition* as equivalent to the correct *classification* of letter-inscriptions. Letter-recognition clearly depends upon a transaction between the writer and the perceiver of a given series of letter-inscriptions, and what the perceiver must do properly in order to recognize an inscription depends in each separate case upon what in particular has been done by the writer. Thus some writers produce script which is much easier to read than the script of other writers; and conversely some readers are more clever at reading poor script than other readers. But what is called for in each case is an adaptation of the reader to the scriptural peculiarities of the writer. In a word, letter-recognition is a transaction between the writer and the perceiver of the symbols in point. But when letter-recognition is thought of merely as a form of classification, it comes to be viewed as a transaction between the perceiver and the symbols themselves. Once one is captured by this way of thinking, the question arises concerning what in particular it is about a given inscription by virtue of which it is the symbol for one letter rather than another. And the natural answer to this question is that the identity of the symbol depends somehow upon its shape or topological characteristics.

It is not surprising that no one has been able to determine quite satisfactorily just what these characteristics might be for the twenty-six letters of our alphabet. In fact there are no such properties. And we would not expect that there *are* such properties if the notion of recognition as a species of classification had not led us to ask the wrong questions. Whether a given inscription represents a given letter is determined, not by the shape of the inscription itself, but by the choice among the twenty-six alternatives on the part of the writer who represented his choice by the inscription in point.

In short, the function which a human reader performs in recognizing the inscriptions composing the line which he reads is one which relates him to the writer, not merely to the inscription itself. It follows that the function we want to be able to build into a mechanical simulator of letter-recognition is one which responds to something human writers do, not merely to the shape of what they write. This seems almost too obvious to say. Yet the classification model of recognition which has dominated practically all current technical thought on the topic of letter-recognition has almost succeeded in hiding it from view.

CHAPTER TWELVE

CODES AND
THE ALPHABET

1. Our account of letter-recognition under the conceptual rubric of Information Theory is incomplete in two respects. For one, there is at first glance an appearance of oddity in the suggestion that letter-recognition should be conceived as if it involved some sort of decoding. This suggestion thus requires clarification. Second, it remains to be specified just what there is about a given letter-symbol by virtue of which it is correct to consider it an inscription of that letter and of no other. These requirements set the task of the present chapter.

If letter-recognition is to be conceived as a matter of decoding, then the letter-inscriptions which are subject to recognition must be conceived as serving in some way as symbols in a code. Now the term 'code' has rather special meaning in some contexts. Cryptographers, for example, often deem it a matter of importance to distinguish between codes and ciphers, the distinction being in the main that with a cipher each separate symbol of the original message is represented separately, while with a code a given code-symbol might stand for a whole phrase or sentence of the original. But this distinction generally has no bearing in contexts other than cryptography. It is quite proper, for instance, to speak of the semaphore code, in which each letter of a message to be conveyed is represented by a distinct position of the sender's arms. In the Morse and international codes, moreover, individual letters are represented not by single symbols, but by series of distinct signals. And it has become customary in the technical parlance of the communication sciences to speak of any transformation of a message into a form suitable for transmission (say into pulses or waveforms) as a codification of the message.[1] In line with this latter use, let us be content to think of any expression of a message in terms of a system of representation expressly suited to a particular channel of communication as a codification of that message.

This broad notion of codification does not in itself remove the appearance of oddity from the thought of letter-recognition as a form of decoding. Three considerations seem to contribute to this appearance. For one thing, in a typical electronic communication system the procedures of encoding and of decoding involve entirely distinct acts, performed with regard to signals which themselves are numerically distinct. Thus the pulses which the telegrapher enters into his transmission line as dots and dashes in the Morse code are different physical occurrences from the signals emanating from the sounder at the other end of the line. In contrast, the letter-inscriptions set down on a page by a writer are numerically identical with the inscriptions which the reader has to interpret. Second is another apparent difference between communication through script and communication through an electronic system which at first may appear more damaging to our account of letter-recognition. In the previous chapter a

---

[1] See, for example, *Information Theory, with Applications to Radar*, by P. M. Woodward (London, Pergamon Press, Ltd., 1953), pp. 71, 73.

distinction was made between the *choice* among possible alternative message states and the *encoding* of that choice for transmission to a potential receiver. According to this distinction, it would be possible for the sender in a particular case to make a choice which he did not encode, or to make an improper encoding of a particular choice. The latter possibility accounted for errors of transmission of one sort within the communication transaction. Now errors of this sort cannot be accounted for if no distinction is made between the choice of a message state by the sender and his encoding of that choice. At first glance, this may seem to be just what we have to contend with in our account of letter-inscribing and letter-reading respectively as instances of encoding and decoding. We may ask, in brief, whether it is not the case that when a person writes a letter symbol on a page it is the letter itself which is his choice, in this case a choice out of twenty-six possibilities. If so, then his choice and his representation of that choice are indistinguishable, and the possibility that he might make an error in coding that choice is not intelligible. Moreover, if the message is not originally coded by the sender, it would seem to make no sense to speak of it as if it required decoding by the receiver.

These two difficulties are easily met. But first let us look at a third difference between our use of script and our use of a device like the Morse code which may appear even more consequential. One notable thing about codes by and large is that they require keys in order to be usable. The purpose of the key is to provide the sender rules for transforming the expression of his message from the ordinary alphabet to the coded form, and to provide the receiver rules for transforming the message in the opposite direction. Moreover, the key is something which has to be committed explicitly either to memory or to a code book in order to be available for use when needed. But no such key, it would appear, is available for use in connection with the ordinary alphabet. More to the point, no such key seems to be required; for in the writing of script there is no transformation from the ordinary alphabet to some other form and back again. This being the case, what can be meant by speaking of the recognition of letters in ordinary script as involving some sort of decoding?

In the estimation of some readers these difficulties will appear (correctly) to be based on misunderstanding. But removal of this misunderstanding will increase the cogency of the Information-Theoretic model. Let us reconsider these difficulties in the order of presentation.

The first alleged difficulty is really not one at all, and the appearance of difficulty can be relieved by shifting the paradigm of codification from the Morse to the semaphore code. In the latter, each letter of the alphabet is represented by a unique combination of positions of two flags held at arms' length (or of two arms extended without flags, etc.). The letter U, for example, is represented by the holding of one's arms in a position approximately 45 degrees above the horizontal on opposite sides of the body. The holding of one's arms in this attitude in appropriate circumstances is precisely the codification of the letter U. But it is likewise precisely this attitude of the sender which the receiver of the message interprets as representing U. The fact that the message state encoded by the sender is numerically identical with the message state decoded by the receiver does not tend to suggest that the semaphore code is not really a code after all, or that the receiver of the message does not really have a job of decoding on his hands.

Whereas the first difficulty was formulated with reference to an identity of the coded signal of the sender and the signal which the receiver decodes, the second involves an alleged identity of the choice of the sender with his encoding of that choice. In the Morse code, it might be contended, the sender chooses in sequence various letters of the alphabet, but his coding of these choices is in terms of series of dots and dashes which are quite distinct from the letters themselves. The charge is that no distinction can be drawn between choice and representation of choice when the medium of communication is the ordinary alphabet, and hence that there is no sense in speaking of that representation as a codification which requires interpretation, or decoding. Now it should be clear that this objection loses whatever force it may at first seem to have if we attend carefully to the distinction between letter-token and letter-type developed in Chapter Ten. The possibilities of choice to which the writer responds with each inscription are those offered by the twenty-six letters of the alphabet. But in speaking of these possibilities, we speak of letter-types. The actual inscription in each case is not one out of twenty-six, but one out of an indefinite number of letter-tokens. In a word, the distinction between the writer's choice and his representation of that choice is just the distinction between a letter-type and one of the letter-tokens which symbolize that type. Thus the choices of the writer in script and the choices of the user of the Morse code are choices from among exactly the same range of possibilities—the letter-types of the ordinary alphabet. The differences between the system of alphabetical inscriptions and the system of dots and dashes provided in the Morse code is merely a matter of the symbols used to represent these choices. In this regard, then, there is no less reason to consider the marks made by a penman as codifications of the alphabet than there is so to consider the dots and dashes with which the telegrapher communicates.

The distinction between letter-type and letter-token also provides the background against which the third diffi-

culty is to be viewed. There are two aspects to this difficulty. First, it is claimed that the use of a code involves
the use of a key, whereas the use of the ordinary alphabet
does not. Second, it is claimed that the purpose of the key
in each case is to provide a transformation between the
code and the alphabet itself, a function for which no need
arises while we are dealing with such standard forms of
representation as those in script writing. Now it must be
admitted from the outset that keys for the use of codes
such as the Morse code can be found in forms which at
first bear little resemblance to any set of instructions ordinarily provided as guides for penmen. A key of this sort
will consist of a list of code symbols paired off with a list
of letter-tokens of the more ordinary kind. But it should
be clear that the *use* of such a key is not limited to transformations between code symbols and alphabetical *symbols* themselves. This use would be typical only in situations where either the sender or the receiver of the coded
message is relatively unfamiliar with the code. In the procedure of the telegrapher, to the contrary, where we can
assume thorough familiarity with the code, there may be
no hint of a transformation from alphabetical symbol to
a symbol in code. Even when concerned with the transmission of messages which are recorded in written English
at either end of the transmission process, the experienced
telegrapher will not be conscious of any direct transition
from written to coded symbol or vice versa. Even more
obviously in the case of the skilled use of semaphore symbols, the business of transferring the message to and from
a conventional written form is inessential to the procedures of the persons involved, and may be entirely lacking as often as not. The point here is simply that the
transformations which are involved in the use of codes
such as we have been considering are not essentially rules
for passing *from* one means of representation to another,

but rather are rules *for* the representation of letter-types. The telegrapher's code sheet, to which if skilled he will seldom refer in practice, provides rules for representing the various letter-types of the alphabet in a form adapted to his medium of communication. It does not merely provide rules for interchanging between alphabetical symbols and dots and dashes. In a fashion which in this respect is entirely parallel, there exists a key for representing letter-types of the Roman alphabet in the form of letter-inscriptions. If this key is seldom reproduced outside of penmanship books, it is only because everyone who knows how to write with this alphabet is thoroughly familiar with it. And the fact that we never or scarcely ever refer to a key of this sort while engaged in the actual business of reading or writing is no more remarkable, and no more threatening to our account, than the fact that skilled telegraphers never or scarcely ever refer to a chart showing the Morse code while exercising their skill.

There is nothing mysterious about the suggestion that the inscriptions of the penman are codifications of the twenty-six letter-types of the alphabet. The fact that the key to this code is not to be found in books dignified by titles like "Operator's Manual," or "The Penman's Code," reflects only the fact that this code is known by all literate users of the language, rather than merely by a special subgroup of language users. And the fact that one does not have to refer to a "code sheet" while writing or reading script is no more noteworthy than the fact that most good telegraphers seldom forget their code. Finally, we have noted that the transformation provided by a key or code book, when one exists, is not essentially between various systems of symbolization, but rather is between the twenty-six letter-types of the alphabet and the particular system of symbolization in point. Exactly the same correspondence exists between these twenty-six letter-types and the system of marks which are inscribed by the penman on his writing surface.

Although no key for the codification of letter-inscriptions exists in any formal representation, the above remarks suggest that such a key might be produced upon demand. This brings us back to the recurrent problem of this essay: What is it about any particular letter-inscription by virtue of which it serves as an inscription of one given letter-type rather than of another or of no letter-type at all? To succeed in answering this question will be in effect to succeed in "decoding the alphabet."

2. The suggestion that the alphabet needs decoding is sufficiently novel to justify both a review of what we as literate users know about the alphabet and a careful statement of what it is that we cannot at this point justly claim to know. If we are average users of the Roman alphabet we can enunciate the twenty-six letters in order, probably reverse as well as forward; we can spell by listing various of these letters in an appropriate fashion, either vocally, in print, or in written script; we can write an inscription corresponding to a given vocally articulated letter-token, or given a written inscription we can articulate a corresponding vocal representation of the letter. We can read passages composed of letter-inscriptions of widely varying shapes, and can sometimes establish the identity of an inscription on the basis of its context where at first it had appeared too poorly formed to be recognizable. We can identify letter-tokens formed in print, in typescript, or inscribed by one of countless penmen no two of which form their letter-inscriptions exactly alike. In a word, we are able to recognize letter-inscriptions of a wide variety of different sizes and shapes.

What we cannot do, or what to this point we have professed not to be able to do, is to say exactly what it is about a particular letter-inscription which makes it correct to identify this inscription as a token of one letter-type and of no other. We are able with minimum probability of error to classify any mark on a written page as being either punctuation, a scribble, or an inscription of a specific one of the twenty-six letter-types. But, as argued in Chapter Three, we are not able to articulate our "principle of classification." Even though we might distinguish, among a small number of inscriptions of a given letter-type, some property or properties possessed by each of these inscriptions immediately at hand, other marks could be formed with these properties which we probably would not identify as inscriptions of this letter-type; and other inscriptions of this letter-type could be formed which do not have these properties.

Thus it is no part of what has been argued thus far to suggest that we are unable to use the alphabet to the fullest extent, or that we are unable to recognize an unlimited number of inscriptions of each of the twenty-six letter-types. Our situation, rather, is that for the most part we simply are unable to say *how* we recognize all the letter-inscriptions which, in fact, we do recognize so easily. In consideration of the group of all properly formed inscriptions of a given letter-type which we would be able to recognize on sight, we are not able to list the properties some or all of which must be present in a given inscription to justify its identification as a token of that letter-type.

Now there is no necessity that we *should* be able to provide such a necessary and sufficient characterization of the indefinitely many inscriptions of any given letter-type. It has been argued, in fact, that if we are limited in our characterization to properties of shape and topology, we *cannot* provide such criteria. But there is no reason why we should be limited in our attempt to characteristics of shape and topology.

It is compatible with our ability to read and write, as argued in Chapter Three, that no characterization in any terms whatsoever can be provided by virtue of which an identification of a token as being of a given letter-type can be justified. But it is equally compatible that a characterization of this sort might be provided in terms other than those of shape and topology. The task of "decoding the alphabet" poses different problems depending upon which alternative is the case. Let us attempt to clarify the two alternatives with paradigms answering to each in turn.

A paradigm for the first alternative must be one in which each of the symbols corresponding to one of the twenty-six letter-types is in itself unanalyzable into any essential characteristics. We may construct a paradigmatic code with respect to which it is clear that the ability to analyze the separate symbols of the code is not essential to the ability to recognize these symbols. An American crayon manufacturer markets a box containing crayons of over fifty different and easily distinguishable colors. Let our code be established by selecting twenty-six of these colors at random, and assigning a different color to each of the twenty-six letter-types of our alphabet according to the order of their selection. The code may be used by marking sequences of colors (any simple shape will do) instead of sequences of letter-inscriptions of the usual sort. In this colorful system, one will learn his "alphabet" by learning which colors represent which of the several letter-types. Note that there is no help for the novice who cannot distinguish among some of the colors concerned. That is, there is no reliable way of *telling* a person how to recognize a given color. He can learn to recognize his colors by learning to imitate the linguistic behavior in this regard of other persons who already know how to recognize them. But there is no analytic description of a color in terms of which one can articulate precisely what it is about a given color patch by virtue of which it *is* of that color and of no other. Hence there is no characterization by which one can articulate what it is about a given color patch by virtue of which it represents a specific letter-type and no other. In the sense of the term in point, colors are unanalyzable. This is to say nothing about the characteristics of physical phenomena which typically accompany the appearance of various colors to the human perceiver. It is to say merely that colors as they appear to people with full faculty of vision are simple qualities which cannot be described correctly and exhaustively in terms of qualities distinct from themselves. In this paradigm, then, the code consists of an established correspondence between the series of twenty-six letter-types and a series of twenty-six symbols, the members of which are unanalyzable.

A paradigm for the second alternative is provided by the Morse code. In the context of this code, each letter-type is represented by series of dots and dashes, varying in length from only one symbol (for E and T) to four. The shape of these symbols is inessential (the dot, for example, might be round, square, diamond-shaped, etc., and the dash rectangular, oblong, etc.). Topology also is inessential (the symbol-figures might be either open or closed). What is obviously essential to the various symbols of the Morse code is the unique ordering of clearly distinguishable elements assigned to each letter.[2] To specify the ordering assigned to any particular letter is to specify the characteristic by virtue of which any codification of that letter corresponds to the letter it codifies. In this paradigm nothing is hidden. It is clear that the essential property of any given codification in the Morse code can be ana-

---

2 See fn. 4, p. 212.

lyzed, and it is clear in any case just what the proper analysis would be. If, in some unusual situation, the problem of "decoding the Morse code" were to arise, the solution would be to specify the unique ordering of dots and dashes essential to each letter-representation within the code.

Which paradigm should we rely upon in pursuing the problem of "decoding the alphabet"? Insofar as our present interest is inspired by the desire to simulate human letter-recognition by mechanical means, this is a question of some importance. If the symbols which serve as letter-tokens in human letter-recognition cannot be analyzed, it follows perforce that they cannot be analyzed in terms of characteristics to which a computer can be programmed to respond. Thus, for example, since the appearance of colors to a typical human observer cannot be analyzed, any attempt to prepare a computer to respond to colors as they appear in this respect would belie a confusion concerning either the capabilities of computers or the nature of apparent colors. Wave patterns of frequencies within the visible range *are* analyzable; but wave patterns are not colors (we see colors, but we do not normally see wave patterns). The best one can say here is that to each distinguishable apparent color there corresponds a limited range of wave frequencies which generally, but not invariably, accompany that apparent color. Thus, if the paradigm of the color code is to guide our enquiry, we must give up the goal of preparing a mechanical system to respond to letter-tokens proper. At best we might hope to find some phenomena which correspond in a more or less regular fashion to the occurrences of these unanalyzable symbols, and which themselves can be analyzed in terms of characteristics which a computer can accommodate. On the other hand, if the paradigm of the Morse code is to be trusted, then the task of simulating human letter-recognition is one of analyzing the letter-tokens themselves, as they typically serve in human recognition, with the hopes of finding characteristics to which a computer can be programmed to respond.

There are several reasons for following the lead of the Morse code paradigm. First, certain obvious groupings exist among letter-tokens formed by most competent penmen which can be accounted for only if the tokens concerned are analyzed into constituent elements. For example, there is an obvious basis in the script of most penmen for grouping together inscriptions of F, G, J, P, Q, Y, and Z, in the lower case; each extends in a loop below the line of inscription. Lower case inscriptions of B, D, F, H, K, and L, likewise share a loop extending upward. Lower case inscriptions of U and W on the one hand, and of M and N on the other, differ primarily with regard to the number of "humps" they embody, while lower case H differs from lower case K only with regard to the "kink" in the final downstroke of the latter. In the case of each grouping, the basis of similarity is a component which seems to be essential to the inscription in a way not characteristic of other components of the concerned inscriptions. This in itself suggests that if we are to discover what is essential in the inscriptions of each of the twenty-six letter-types, we must attend to components of these inscriptions which can be distinguished from other components. In a word, we may expect our vision of what is essential to each letter-token to come clear only with an appropriate analysis of the token into components.

It is a matter of observation, parallel to the consideration above, that certain strokes can literally be removed from a series of well-formed inscriptions without affecting the intelligibility of the script. An experiment anyone can perform for himself is to inscribe a text with soft pencil in clear handwriting, and then to erase all lines in his text which have been inscribed with a backward motion of his pencil. If he then passes this text on to someone who normally has no trouble in reading his handwriting, chances are that this person will be able to read what he has written without a sharp decrease in either speed or accuracy. If all strokes resulting from a forward motion of the pencil are erased, however, more difficulty probably will be encountered in reading the resulting text. This observation adds up to a second reason for believing that some components of our letter-inscriptions are more essential than others, and consequently that an analysis must be undertaken of these symbols if we are to succeed in "decoding the alphabet."

A third consideration which reinforces this belief concerns the way in which children are taught to form proper letter-inscriptions in grade school. A penmanship manual consists in more than a list of twenty-six different line configurations. It includes, in addition, instructions for forming these configurations; and these instructions proceed with reference to constituent elements within each inscription. The child is taught to write a lower case A on the basis of a hand motion resulting in a series of counterclockwise ovals, the same motion which is basic to the lower case D, G and Q. Other letter-inscriptions begin with an upward sweep in a clockwise direction, and yet others contain straight strokes slanted slightly off vertical. These characteristics result from hand motions reinforced by well-known exercises of the penmanship manual. A child can learn to "build up" an F, a G, an H, and most other letter-tokens, by beginning with one basic stroke, followed by another, and so on. This would be impossible if the concerned letter-tokens, like colors, were not susceptible to analysis into constituent elements. Colors are learned only by the showing of examples; but letter-inscriptions can be learned piecemeal, beginning as it were with the "basic strokes." Since the learning of the system of script writing is considerably more like learning the Morse code than like learning colors, it is reasonable to suspect that the use of this system also more resembles the use of the former than the use of the latter.

This discussion has been intended to establish that our best chances of determining what is essential in any given letter-inscription lies with the conception that each inscription is subject to analysis into a small number of components, and that the differences among various inscriptions have to do with the selection and ordering of these elements.

3. It has been argued that the letter-symbols inscribed by a penman who writes in "ordinary script" might be conceived justly as codifications of the twenty-six letter-types of the Roman alphabet. It has been argued further that each of these symbols is analyzable into a small number of basic components, just as the various symbols in the Morse code can be analyzed into dots and dashes. Continuing with the paradigm of the Morse code, we may expect that the essential differences among the various letter-inscriptions of the penman reside in the ordering of these basic components. Let us consider further what to expect regarding the nature of these components.

One difference which appears immediately between the symbols of the Morse code and the symbols of normal handwriting in script (in contrast with hand-printed characters) is that the former are composed of discrete elements, either visual or auditory, while the latter are composed largely of unbroken lines and curves. Although different penmen habitually introduce breaks at different points in their written line, and an individual penman might break his line at different places on different occasions, complete breaks in the written line generally occur only at the ends of words and in the formation of some capital letters (like H and K) and of some special marks (like dots for the I and crosses for the T). Thus we may conceive a series of handwritten letters as consisting by and large of various deformations of an unbroken cursive line directed from the left to the right of the penman. Some of these deformations amount to loops, either above or below the line, others consist of concave or convex arcs followed by discontinuities in the cursive line, while others are merely strokes serving primarily to connect adjacent letters. It is among deformations of this sort that the basic components of handwritten letter-inscriptions are to be sought.

An attempt has been made by the author to "decode the alphabet" in terms of deformations of this sort. The results are reported in the Appendix in the form of an alphabetic code.[3] Six easily distinguishable stroke-formations, in addition to the blank, serve as components in this code, and each letter-symbol is analyzed as containing three of these components. Thus to each letter-type of the Roman alphabet there corresponds, under this conception, a unique ordered triad of these basic cursive elements. What is essential to any given letter-token is that it exemplify in visible symbols one of these twenty-six distinct triads.

It must be emphasized that this particular analysis of letter-symbols into triads of cursive elements is suggested only as a provisional analysis of cursive writing. Not all penmen use the same system of symbolization in script, and not all penmen write intelligibly all of the time. Con-

---

[3] The Appendix was considered a more appropriate place for this material, since the method used in this decoding attempt was more a matter of trial and error than of conceptual analysis. Moreover, it is entirely likely that obvious mistakes and oversights in these results will appear when the code is put into practice with an operating letter-recognition mechanism.

sequently this analysis will not hold for all script samples, granted even that it holds for some. This analysis, moreover, has no relevance to symbols imparted to a page by a printing press or typewriter. The essential difference between handwritten and printed letter-symbols (even those printed in pseudo-script) lies in the fact that the former possesses a temporal dimension entirely lacking in the latter. In the printing of a letter-symbol, either by typewriter or by press, the entire symbol is laid upon the page more or less simultaneously. So with regard to the actual printing of the symbol there is no matter of a serial ordering among various parts. More importantly, the formation of the symbol itself has nothing to do with the progress of a cursive line across a page. Hence there is nothing essentially temporal about the formation of such a symbol. Although printing a symbol in this fashion takes time, it is irrelevant whether all the symbol is printed at one instant or, if not, whether one part is printed before any other. Thus, it would appear, the analogy of the color code is more in line with the fashion in which printed letters symbolize the twenty-six letter-types of the alphabet.

With the formation of handwritten inscriptions, however, both the sequential ordering of the several components and the direction of flow of the cursive line in the inscription of these components are taken to be essential to the identity of the resulting symbol. In a word, the basic components of letter-inscriptions are not merely lines and shapes, but rather directional strokes. The articulation of these inscriptions consequently requires reference both to spatial and to temporal characteristics of the cursive line.

In view of this, it is no surprise that letter-inscriptions cannot be analyzed in terms merely of shape and topological features, for features of both sorts are entirely atemporal. The way out of the conceptual impasse of Chapter Three is in the direction of admitting a temporal dimension as well as a spatial dimension in our conception of the nature of handwritten letter-inscriptions. This temporal dimension is an important factor in the letter-recognition technique outlined in the final chapter of this book.

CHAPTER' THIRTEEN

TOWARDS MECHANICAL
LETTER-RECOGNITION

1. Letter-recognition has been discussed thus far as a function performed by human beings capable of sense perception. Let us now abstract from our conception of letter-recognition those details which seem to reflect a uniquely human activity. We may hope to find remaining the outlines of a function which is within the capabilities of existing data-processing mechanisms.

The term 'function' has been reserved in this essay to designate a relationship between two sets of events, S_1 and S_2, such that the occurrence of a particular event in S_1 regularly increases the probability of occurrence of some event within a particular subset of S_2. Depending upon context, it may be appropriate to think of members of S_1 and S_2 respectively as cause and effect, as stimulus and response, as independent and dependent variables, as input and output, or in yet some other pairwise fashion. In general, a system which under certain conditions produces a predictable occurrence within S_2 given a particular occurrence within S_1 has the function of transforming occurrences of S_1 into occurrences of S_2 under these conditions.

[273

Now the human being capable of recognizing letter-inscriptions may be conceived as a system which performs a function of this sort. The task of simulating human letter-recognition accordingly has been conceived as the task of providing a mechanical system which performs the same transformation between the same input and output classes as that performed by the human system.

Let us at this juncture consider an objection which, if sustained, would make it pointless to continue. One of the main burdens of the discussion thus far has been to show that recognition is an attainment, while classification is a process, and that, since attainments and processes are activities of fundamentally different types, any mechanical system which merely classifies is a poor bet as the basis for a simulation of recognition. The anticipated objection at this point is that, by the very nature of the data-handling procedures of our computing machines, they are capable of performing *only* processes. It might be pointed out, in a word, that data-processing *is* a process. And if recognition, being an attainment, cannot be simulated by processes, there might appear to be good reason, not for attempting to improve upon existing "recognition mechanisms," but rather to give up altogether the hope of simulating the human function of letter-recognition.

This is an important point, and it is important consequently to see clearly why it does not in fact constitute an objection. High-speed electronic computers, like computers of any other sort, are data-processing systems. To process data is at least to perform a systematic sequence of operations with the end in view of discovering or of displaying certain relationships among the data. The performance of these operations, whether it be mechanical as with a desk calculator, manual as with a pencil or abacus, or electronic as with modern computers, is a matter which necessarily involves doing something sequentially and in time, and which thus fits the definition of 'process' expressly adopted in Chapter Four. Does it follow from this that any function performed by a computer must be classified as a process? Clearly it does not. To say what we have just said about data-processing and computers is to say merely that the operations of a computer are processes. So, presumably, are the operations of any other system. The operations of the system of neurons and synapses in the cerebral cortex, which surely contribute in some way to almost all human behavior, are themselves processes. But this does not prevent humans from perceiving, from recognizing, or in a variety of other ways from performing acts which count as attainments rather than processes within our categorization. The human being does many things with the support of his sensory organs and brain. Some of the things he does amount to processes, such as looking and scanning; but other things he does amount to attainments, such as recognizing. The distinction between processes and attainments within the range of human activities is not erased by the observation that the operations of the sensory organs and of the brain involve processes.

Similarly, the fact that the operations of an electronic computer involve processes leaves entirely open the possibility that some things computers do, or might do, would count as attainments in every respect relevant for our purposes. Among tasks assigned to computers in typical research and industrial applications are those of ordering, sorting, classifying, and of performing routine arithmetical operations. These are processing tasks. But to speak of the process of sorting, for example, is not to refer simply to the *operations* (rapid alterations of electronic states) of the computer which performs the process, but rather is to refer to the *function* performed. There are other functions performed by computers which are clearly attainments in our sense of the term. And the fact that this is the case is quite in harmony with the fact that the operations by which these functions are performed are data-processing operations. Computers not only can add, but when properly programmed can detect errors in their own addition when errors occur. Detection of an error is an attainment. Computers can discriminate radar data originating with moving aircraft against a background of radar data containing mostly "noise." This also is an attainment. Computers can tune radios, can guide space probes to their destination, and can repair themselves by changing their own circuitry. Among applications with more popular appeal, we now have computers which can prove mathematical and logical theorems and computers which can win at chess. All of these results are attainments in our sense of the word.

Attainment is not exclusively a human prerogative. And no attainment is achieved without the support of some processing system. Neither fact tends to blur the distinction between processes and attainments. Our present concern is to simulate the human attainment of letter-recognition; and the fact that both the human being and his mechanical counterpart in this attainment are data-processing systems neither increases nor decreases the difficulty of this task.

Our task, in the terminology of Chapter One, is not to *replicate* human letter-recognition, but rather to *simulate* it. So it is not essential, and perhaps not even possible, that the transformation accomplished by the simulating system involve exactly the same operations as those involved in the accomplishment of letter-recognition by a human perceiver. But we should not be disturbed by the observation that the mechanical counterpart of this transformation must involve *some* operations.

What *is* essential for the successful simulation of human letter-recognition is that we have a clear conception of both the input and the output of the human function, and that we have a clear conception of the structure of the transformation by which the function is accomplished. Let us briefly review the results of the preceding chapters as they bear upon these requirements.

In general, of course, the input to the human function of letter-recognition is the inscription of the various letter-symbols available within our written language, and the output is some act of reading or of identification in which these symbols serve according to the intentions governing their original inscription. But these general notions of input and output are too diffuse to advance the cause of mechanical letter-recognition. This became obvious in our review of "the state of the art" at the beginning of this essay. An attempt to focus these notions into workable concepts led to the Information-Theoretic model developed in Chapter Eleven. In light of this model, letter-recognition has been conceived as the reception of information committed to letter-symbols with their inscription. The two language-users involved in this communication transaction thus are related as sender and receiver, and the communication link between them consists of the letter-symbols which originate with an act by the sender and which discharge their information (without losing it) with an act by the receiver. In line with the distinction between type and token offered in Chapter Ten, each letter-symbol may be conceived as a token representing (in the Roman alphabet) one of twenty-six different letter-types. The inscription of a given letter-token serves to record a choice by the sender from among these twenty-six different letter-types. Since in general the probability that any given one of these twenty-six letter-types will be chosen is unique, notification of the actual choice of any one letter-type conveys a unique amount of information. It is in this sense, more fully developed in Chapter Twelve, that the inscription of a given letter-token imparts to that symbol an informational content which is unladen with the recognition of the symbol for what it represents.

In this summary sketch of the transaction between writer and reader the input and the output of the recognition function stand in clear view. The input is the representation of a given choice among letter-types in terms of a code of symbols especially available for that purpose. By virtue of this representation, the letter-symbol takes on a particular information content of which the reader is notified when he recognizes the symbol. The output of the letter-recognition function, then, is the detection of the information imparted to individual letter-symbols with their inscription. With the act of recognition, the reader comes to interpret the letter-token as representing the selfsame letter-type selected by the writer.

The input to the letter-recognition function is the inscription of a symbol with a unique information content. The output of the function is the detection of the information imparted with the inscription. We turn next, in review, to the structure of the transformation accomplished by the function.

Now it is a safe working hypothesis that no mechanical system will be constructed which accomplishes this transformation just as human beings do through operations of sense perception. Human sense perception may be simulated, but in any sober view it must appear at least highly dubious that it will ever be replicated. This gives justification for withholding the phrase 'sense perception' and cognates from any literal description of mechanical procedures. Because of the involvement of human recognition with sense perception, examined in Part Three above, someone might even wish, when speaking strictly, to conjecture that mechanical systems will never be capable of the recognition function. This, however, is primarily a matter of terminology, and does not shake our resolution to *simulate* the function of letter-recognition performed by human beings. For the requirements of this task do not include the replication of human recognitive behavior. The requirements rather are to produce a mechanical system capable of achieving a transformation over the same input and output classes comparable in desired respects to that achieved in human letter-recognition. One result of importance stemming from the Information-Theoretic model is that there need be nothing essentially human about the output of this transformation.

Just as human letter-recognition may be conceived as a transaction between two human language-users, the corresponding mechanical transaction may be conceived as a transaction between a human and a mechanical system prepared for a comparable use of the language. In either case, the successful completion of the transaction is the detection of information committed to a letter-symbol or series of letter-symbols by the act of a human penman. The task of simulating human letter-recognition accordingly amounts to that of providing mechanical detection techniques whereby the conventional letter-tokens used by humans for communication through the written word may be made to yield their information content. What is required, in a nutshell, is a mechanical *detection* system.

There is a natural shift from the concept of recognition to the concept of detection. Both, of course, are concepts with several allegiances. But just as a use of the term 'recognition' was found which fell in nicely with our purposes in talking about the reception of information which has been given symbolic representation, an established use of 'detection' may be marshaled for the same purpose. Thus, for example, radio engineers speak of detectors, the function of which is to accomplish the demodulation of an incoming signal, thereby extracting from the carrier wave its information content. In this sense of the term, human beings function as detectors in their recognition of letter-symbols. And in this sense of the term again, our requirement is for a mechanical means of performing the same function without the perceptual facilities of the human recognizer.

Conception of the task in this light is an advantage in itself. As long as the concept of recognition retains its overtones of human perceptual activity, the notion of a mechanism which literally can *recognize* letter-inscriptions conveys something of the sense of paradox. But the concept of a mechanism which can *detect* the information content of a set of conventional symbols seems refreshingly straightforward.

This shift from the concept of recognition to the concept of detection opens a new approach towards the simulation of human recognitive behavior. It is important to be sure, however, that with this shift we do not change the nature of our simulation problem. Let us retrace the main outlines of the analysis in Part Two, to see that 'recognition' shares with 'detection' those properties relevant to the simulation task.

2. In terms of traditional logic, the concepts of detection and of recognition as we have developed them under the Information-Theoretic model are related as genus and species. Thus the shift from the concept of recognition to the concept of detection is not a shift from the notion of something that people but not machines can do to the notion of something that can be done by machines but not by people. It is, instead, a shift from the concept of doing something the way people do it to the concept of doing what in other respects is much the same thing in a way which is open to both men and machines. The phrase 'letter-recognition' covers the way persons capable of sense

perception detect the information content of letter-inscriptions. But when, according to the task set down at the beginning of this chapter, we abstract from the concept of letter-recognition what is uniquely within the capabilities of human perceivers, we are left with the concept of a function which can be performed by nonhuman means as well. This is the function of information detection.

Thus the term 'recognition', when applied to the uniquely human response to a set of conventional letter-symbols, signifies detection of the information represented by those symbols through the (poorly understood) operations of sense perception, while the term 'decoding' or one of its equivalents, as applied to the mechanical response to a set of conventional symbols, signifies detection of the information represented by those symbols by the (well-understood) operations of a mechanical detection device. Where 'recognition' signifies the human way of extracting information from a set of symbols, the terms 'decoding', or simply 'detection' itself, may serve to signify the extraction of information with reference to the performance of either human or mechanical systems.

'Detection' shares with 'recognition' all the logical characteristics which served to mark in Chapter Four the distinction between processes and attainments, and which therefore should be retained in a satisfactory simulation of the function of letter-recognition. Both 'recognition' and 'detection' signify acts which, although datable, have no duration and accordingly no distinct beginning or end. Whereas, for example, the question 'When did you finish checking the figures?' makes good sense in many ordinary contexts, neither 'When did you finish recognizing the mistake?' nor 'When did you finish detecting the error?' would normally be intelligible questions. Again, both 'recognition' and 'detection' typically signify acts the accomplishment of which results in some increase in the capabilities of the accomplishing agent. The man who recognized a landmark in strange territory can proceed more directly along his way after than before recognition, and a man or machine which detects an error in procedure can indicate whether and where a mistake in procedure occurs. More to the point, either the man or the machine which detects the information contained within a given symbol can specify after detection, but not before, which actual choice among possible choices is represented by the symbol in question.

Finally, in Chapter Four, we noted that attainments typically occur "in full measure" if they occur at all. Although a horse might run halfheartedly, he cannot win halfheartedly. And, while either a man or a machine might slowly and methodically, or hastily and inefficiently, file through a series of symbolic notations, there is no such thing as a slow or hasty, methodical or inefficient, detection of an error in notation. And neither, for that matter, is there such a thing as a slow, halfhearted, or inefficient, detection of the content of an information-laden symbol. Detection, like winning and recognizing, is an "all or nothing" affair. It follows from this, and on other grounds as well, that neither recognition nor detection consists of a set of procedures some part of which might be satisfactorily accomplished without the satisfactory accomplishment of the remainder. In particular, neither recognition nor detection is the sequential application of a series of criteria for class membership, all of which or perhaps only some of which might be met in a given case. Procedures of some sort unquestionably are involved in any act of attainment, whether human or mechanical. But no set of procedures in themselves exhaustively constitute the human function of detection, and so it must be with the mechanical simulation of that function. In other words, we may say that the output of the detection function is not merely the state of having completed a series of procedures, but rather is an attainment the mark of which is something that can be done and not merely something that has been done.

This connects with facets of the distinction drawn in Chapter Five between perceptual and decisional attainments, which likewise may be given cursory review. It was argued there that neither recognition nor detection, being typical of perceptual attainments of the human being, are subject to command. Thus a man or a machine which failed to detect an error, or failed to detect the information content of a conventional symbol, could not for that reason alone sensibly be accused of disobedience. But failure to execute a series of procedures might count as disobedience in many common circumstances. This suggests for our purposes that not all the hazards in the business of information detection can be removed by any set of instructions to the human or to the mechanical detection system, no matter how sophisticated and comprehensive these instructions may be. The type of flexibility to encourage in the development of an adequate detection mechanism, in particular, is not in the direction of an increasingly large number of specific instructions (whether provided by the programmer or by the machine itself) to cover a larger number of eventualities with which the machine might have to cope, but rather in the direction of more general instructions which allow the operations of the machine to reflect more directly the unique constraints of each letter-recognition problem. As noted in Chapter Five, it is the case in general that an attainment like recognition or detection is not the result of any specific process the undertaking of which is a prerequisite for achieving that result. In contrast with attainments of a decisional sort which as a rule are the desired outcome of some specific process (as deciding concludes the process of deliberating), detection is not the predictable outcome of any particular set of procedures. We obviously want, nonetheless, to provide our detection system with a set of operating procedures which enable it to proceed in a reliable fashion to the attainment of detection whenever possible.

It is time to translate these general remarks into a description of a possible mechanism capable of detecting the information content of the conventional symbols inscribed by competent human penmen. The description which follows is neither a mechanical nor a complete operational specification of such a mechanism. There is no claim that it is the best system conceivable along these lines, or even that it is a comparatively good system. Any such claim would have to be checked out in practice, and hence would be idle in the present context. The description below is intended only to illustrate how the theoretical discussion of the pages preceding might be turned to practical use.

3. A detection system capable of decoding a conventional symbol must be able to apply in reverse the same coding conventions as those governing the original encoding of the symbol. If, for example, the detection system is a human telegrapher, he must know the code in terms of which the incoming signals are formulated. And if the detection system, whether human or mechanical, is to extract the information content of symbols in a conventional written language, it must be able to apply the same conventions of representation which governed the original inscription of the symbols.

It has been argued that the various letter-symbols by which competent penmen represent the twenty-six letter-types of the Roman alphabet can be analyzed into short sequences of cursive elements. Since a different sequence corresponds uniquely to each letter-type, these sequences collectively may be conceived as a code for the unambiguous representation of any of the corresponding letter-types. The *inscription* of one of these sequences is the codification of a choice among the twenty-six letter-types, which thereby is represented by the resulting letter-token. The *detection* of the information content of such a token accordingly is the decodification of the letter-token.

The detection of the information conveyed by a given letter-token thus is tantamount to the articulation of the symbol into the same code-elements as those which were combined with its inscription, under the guidance of the same coding conventions. The basic requirements of our mechanical detection system then are (1) that it be able to articulate letter-symbols originating with human penmen in terms of the same code-elements entering into the inscription of the symbols, and (2) that it be provided with the same coding conventions as those governing the inscription. The code discussed in Chapter Twelve and in the Appendix is an example of what is required by (2). We have now to consider one way in which requirement (1) might be met by a mechanical detection system. What follows is a general description of a possible detection system which meets the conceptual specifications of our previous analysis of letter-recognition, considered in abstraction from any involvement with human sense perception.

The input to this detection system is a series of letter-tokens inscribed or assumed to have been inscribed by a human penman. There are no time limits placed upon the time of inscription of the tokens relative to the time of input.[1] Also, there are no requirements regarding size,

---

[1] This removes an important restriction on some of the best work thus far reported on the problem of script recognition. In "Machine Reading of Cursive Script," *Information Theory*, ed. Colin Cherry (London, Butter-

position, or orientation of the series of letter-tokens. It is assumed, however, that the letter-tokens are written in cursive script, rather than in printed form.

The successful output of the system is a series of symbols formed by the system itself which, with reference to the code governing the formation of such symbols, represents in order the same letter-types as those represented by the letter-tokens presented to the system as input. When this correspondence exists between input and output symbols, we may say that the symbols presented to the system have been *matched*.

The role of the input symbol, it should be noted, is not to serve as an object to be classified (for which function the system is not prepared), but rather is to serve as a guide in the formation of matching symbols by the system itself. When a symbol presented to the system has been successfully matched by a symbol generated by the system, the information conveyed by the former symbol has been recovered and the communication transaction inaugurated by the penman who inscribed that symbol has been completed. This accords with the result of our analysis of letter-recognition in light of the Information-Theoretic model, according to which the recognition of a letter-inscription by a human reader was asserted to be equivalent to the perception of the inscription conjoined with the ability to reproduce it.[2] In our mechanical simulation, perception of the inscription is replaced with a stable representation of the symbol within the system, and ability to reproduce the symbol by hand is replaced by a comparable ability on the part of the machine.

---

worth and Co., Ltd., 1961), p. 316, for example, the authors L. S. Frish-kopf and L. D. Harmon state "that an attempt to solve the problems inherent in recognition of already-written script might indeed have discouraged us altogether."

2 See pp. 249 ff.

We have now to consider how the machine might be enabled to reproduce, or to match, the letter-symbols which it receives as input. In the illustrative code of the Appendix, each letter-symbol is an ordered triad of code-elements, and there are in all (including the blank) seven different elements. Each element is given a very general definition in terms of directional change of the vector tangent to the line, and each element could show up with a variety of different shapes within a given line of inscribed symbols. The directional characteristics of these elements reflect a temporal dimension which is explicit at the time of their inscription, but which is no longer explicit when the symbols are considered merely as marks on a page. This temporal dimension becomes explicit again with the formation by the system of matching symbols in terms of the same cursive elements. Since, as argued in the preceding chapter, this temporal dimension is essential in the formation of letter-inscriptions, it must be essential also in their reproduction.[3]

Of the 120 different triads that might be formed according to the provisions of symbol formation within the code,[4] only twenty-six (or a few more to allow alternative symbolizations in some cases) serve to represent letter-types. The task of the system is to formulate, for any given letter-token input, an instance of one of these triads *which*

---

[3] In *IRE Transactions on Information Theory* (February 1962), pp. 160–166, a handwriting recognition system is described by Murray Eden which is similar to ours in that recognition of symbols is achieved through the generation of comparable symbols. The present system differs from Eden's insightful contribution in two important respects: (1) his code is "inflated" (the letter-token M, e.g., requires ten distinct elements for its formation); and (2) the elements of his code, although they are called "strokes" (p. 161), are essentially line-segments the shape and orientation of which are of primary importance. Direction of cursive flow in the formation of these elements does not appear to be an essential factor in their formation; and if it is thought to be, there is no reason within his theory why it should be essential.

[4] See p. 300.

in terms of the code represents the same letter-type as the input symbol.

Formation of matching symbols by the system occurs within a matrix (hereafter "Matrix") of binary memory units ordered by x, y coordinates. The configuration of an input symbol is represented within this Matrix as if it were reflected in a mirror marked off by evenly spaced horizontal and vertical lines. Each memory unit serves as an area on the "mirror grid." If a given unit contains part of the "reflection" of the configuration, it is given a *plus* value; all units not "reflecting" part of the configuration retain a *minus* value. Thus each symbol which can be uniquely represented within the Matrix can be represented also by a unique series of *plus* and *minus* values of the units ordered according to their position within the Matrix. Input symbols can be represented within the Matrix in differing degrees of resolution; the more memory units occupied with the representation of a given symbol, the greater the resolution of that representation. When a line of symbols first is presented to the system, several symbols within the line are represented in their given sequence within the Matrix, on the basis of which representation are determined both the direction of the written line and the base line with reference to which each of the input symbols is approximately positioned. When the base line and direction of the series of symbols have been determined, the individual symbols within the series are represented singly in greater resolution for matching.

The values of the memory units can be controlled as well by a sub-system, called "the Stroke Originator," which generates the code-elements out of which the system forms matching triads. The function of the Stroke Originator is to form cursive lines which fall within the defined limits of the code elements. What is essential, in the case of each of these elements, is the clockwise directionality of the stroke and the continuity or lack of continuity of the cursive line as the stroke is terminated. Instances of each of the six articulated elements share no particular shape in common, but can trace out any cursive line within the limits established by the definition of the element. This provision allows considerable flexibility in matching the strokes of different penmen, and is in accord with the conclusion argued above that there is no particular shape which is essential for the tokens of any given letter-type.

Lines generated by the Stroke Originator are ordered into triads by another sub-system called "the Stroke Sequencer." Only triads which can be construed as code-representations of one of the twenty-six letter-types are allowed; but in the absence of further constraints, triads are selected at random. Further constraints come in the form of fedback information about successful and unsuccessful attempts to match particular input symbols in the Matrix.

The actual matching takes place under the control of a further sub-system designated "the Comparator." The function of the Comparator is to duplicate as much as possible of the representation of the input symbol in the Matrix with the triad of strokes which in a particular instance has been selected by the Stroke Sequencer. The input symbol is represented, as noted above, by an ordered series of *plus* and *minus* values. As each part of the representation in turn is duplicated by one of the strokes or part of one of the strokes generated by the Stroke Originator under the control of the Stroke Sequencer, the particular memory units containing that part of the representation are changed from *plus* to *minus*. The operation of matching begins by causing the first stroke in the selected triad to trace out as much of the representation of the input symbol as possible without violating the definition of that particular stroke. When the first stroke can trace the representation no further, the second stroke in the triad is brought into play for continued tracing of the configuration. Finally, the third stroke is used to trace out whatever of the remainder of the configuration it can follow. If the three strokes in sequence have traced out the entire configuration, nothing will remain of the representation of that symbol in the Matrix: all *plus* values will have been changed to *minus*. Since triads are formed at random by the Sequencer, within the constraints of the code, it will be the case more frequently that only part, and perhaps very little, of the representation of the input symbol in the Matrix will have been traced by a particular sequence of strokes. If it can be determined after application of the first or second stroke of a particular triad that the triad as a whole will not match a given input, the Comparator instructs the Sequencer to eliminate that triad from the list of possible matches for this input and to provide another possible triad to the Comparator for testing. If all three strokes of a triad trace out some part of the representation, but not all of it, the Comparator measures the disparity between input configuration and partially matching triad in terms of the number of memory units not randomly connected which retain their original *plus* value. A controlled variable number (n) will serve as the boundary between matching and failure to match on the part of a given triad. The value of n might be controlled either by the programmer or by the system itself as it becomes adapted to the peculiarities of a particular penman's script.

In some cases, one or more of the set of all permissible triads will be found to trace out a good part of the input configuration without effecting an acceptable match. If the Comparator does not indicate a clear preference among these partial matches, a decision will be made by a further sub-system called "the Contextual Discriminator" as to which partial match is most likely to correspond to the actual input symbol. This decision is made on the basis of known statistics regarding redundancy of the written language, and often will not be made until there have been a number of successful attempts to match further members of the series of symbols presented to the system. When a decision of this sort is made by the Contextual Discriminator, the system cannot be said to have detected the information-content of the symbol in question. We should say, rather, that information obtained by other means has been used to identify the symbol. The utility of such identifications is to provide indications of peculiarities in the script of a given penman that might help the system adapt to his style of stroke formation.

If the system fails in this fashion to match a relatively high proportion of the symbols in a given penman's script, we can only say that the system is not prepared to communicate with that penman. This might be remedied in some cases by changing the code under which the penman is assumed to have inscribed his letter-tokens, or by altering the rules under which the Comparator operates to accommodate unusual penmanship. It is always possible, however, that the penman's inscriptions are so unusually formed or so poorly formed that the system cannot be made to respond to them. This, of course, is a possibility to which human readers also are liable.

The response of this system to a given letter-token input shares all the characteristics found to be essential to human letter-recognition, save only those characteristics directly dependent upon human capabilities of sense perception. Corresponding to the ability of a human being to perceive a letter-token, in turn, is the ability of the mechanical system to receive a letter-token as input and to represent it in an orderly and stable fashion for further processing. Parallel to the human ability to reproduce a letter-token in script upon recognizing it is the machine's ability to reproduce a letter-token upon detecting it through the operation of its stroke-formation capabilities. Thus, whereas human recognition of a letter-inscription amounts to the perception of that inscription given the ability to reproduce it either vocally or in script, mechanical detection of the inscription amounts to the representation of the inscription within its Matrix and the ability to reproduce it by the Stroke Originator.

It may be emphasized again that the function of the system is not to classify a letter-symbol, but rather to match it. Correct matching of the symbol constitutes detection of the information conveyed by it, and hence corresponds to human recognition of the symbol. The function of the system, then, is an attainment rather than merely a process. And like other attainments, this is marked by an ability present with the system after but not before the matching—namely, the ability to represent the same letter-type as that represented by the human penman according to the same coding conventions. Like other attainments, moreover, detection of the information conveyed by the input symbol is an "all or nothing" affair. As the system is constructed, either the input symbol is satisfactorily matched, or it is not matched at all; and only in the first case does the system extract information from the symbol. When identification is made on grounds other than an acceptable matching according to an explicit code, no information is gained by the system through its confrontation with the symbol.

Thus it is that the major outlines of this system derive from the major conclusions of the preceding analysis of human letter-recognition.

4. It might be objected that the system described above has not itself really broken away from the classifica-

tion model of recognition which has been extensively belabored throughout this essay. For, it might be suggested, the problem of letter-recognition has merely been shifted from the problem of classifying whole letter configurations to the problem of classifying different elements within letter configurations. If this is the case, then the function performed by the system remains essentially one of classification.

This objection cannot be sustained, for there is nothing in the procedures of this detection system which involves an actual segmentation of the input symbol into constituent elements. The various symbols formed by the system as possible matches for a given input symbol are themselves constructed out of discrete cursive elements. But the actual matching or failure to match occurs in any given case with respect to the symbol as a whole. There is a sense in which the input symbol might be said to have been segmented *by* a successful match with a triad constructed by the system. With a successful match, only part of the input symbol will be traced by the first cursive element in the triad, and different parts will be traced by the second and the third elements in turn. The procedure of tracing out these various parts of the input symbol, however, does not itself involve a prior segmentation of the symbol; and in the case of an unsuccessful matching attempt, the input symbol simply is not segmented at all. There is no sense in which this procedure can be considered a comparison between two sets of previously segmented symbols, and hence no sense in which the procedure might correctly be said to involve a classification of the various elements which might be considered parts of the configuration of the input symbol.[5]

---

[5] Compare the recognition of a line-drawing as a dog by Thurber. *After* identifying the picture, one can begin to isolate various parts of the animal's anatomy. But surely one does not *begin* to identify the picture by isolating various members and classifying each in turn as a specific part of a "Thurberesque dog."

It is noteworthy, in fact, that the problem of segmentation does not arise in the context of our method of detection. It is not necessary prior to the processing of a series of input symbols either to divide the series into separate symbols or to divide the separate symbols into distinct parts. In this system, each symbol in a series is matched if possible before subsequent symbols are even considered, and segmentation into elements occurs as a matter of course as the system succeeds in its matching attempt. Segmentation thus occurs as a result of the detection procedure, and is not a prerequisite as in the case of a classification system.

When letter-recognition is conceived under the model of classification, however, the problem of segmentation becomes critical.[6] For if a system is to identify individual letter-symbols by classifying them according to some fixed set of characteristics, it is necessary to separate individual letters out of the written line before they can be presented

---

[6] Frishkopf and Harmon, as an example, in *Information Theory*, make an attempt to classify letter-symbols according to whether they possess certain combinations of characteristics such as retrograde strokes, cusps and closure. In order to apply these criteria, it is necessary first to divide a line of symbols into individual components. The authors suggest several methods which are partially successful, applied either separately or in combination, but express dissatisfaction with any method they had devised at the time (pp. 305–306). B. W. White, presumably writing prior to the publication of the above paper by Frishkopf and Harmon, remarks that no computer recognition program "has tackled the problem of segmentation. In every case, it is assumed that there is but one letter, one vowel, one pattern in the computer to be recognized." He goes on to say that the "Morse code program described by Selfridge [with Neisser, in "Pattern Recognition by Machine," *Scientific American,* August 1960] is almost the only recognition program which deals with such segmentation problems, and it is significant that a large part of the processing done in this program is devoted to segmentation—isolating the sequence of dots and dashes to be recognized." White's remark is in "Studies of Perception," *Computer Applications in the Behavioral Sciences,* ed. Harold Borko (Englewood Cliffs, N.J., Prentice-Hall, 1962), p. 300. Another comment by White in the location cited is true in a timeless way: "It is impossible to be involved in the construction of such a computer program without being forced to consider many facets of human pattern recognition and perception from a very different viewpoint."

for classification. The designer of such a system accordingly is faced with the task of providing a procedure for separating symbols out of a sequence before it can be determined what letters these symbols represent or even whether they are letter-symbols at all. In other words, the symbols must be identified *as* letter-symbols before it can be determined *what* letter-types they symbolize. It is not surprising that no satisfactory way has been found to do this, since the very notion of doing it borders on paradox.

Rather than having to isolate individual letter-symbols from a series *in order* to identify them, however, our system isolates them *by* identifying them. Thus a severe problem for previous attempts to simulate letter-recognition is removed by adopting a conceptual model in which the problem does not arise. This is but one further advantage of our concept of recognition over recognition conceived as a form of classification.

APPENDIX

DECODING
THE ALPHABET

It is convenient to conceive the Morse code as a series of symbols composed of three elements, the dot, the dash and the blank, arranged in ordered quadruples. Since the blank can occur only in the last three places, a total of fifty-four different symbols can be formed in this fashion. Of these, twenty-six represent letters of the alphabet. The Braille code similarly can be conceived as consisting of ordered sextuples of two elements (the dot and the blank), either of which can appear in any of the six positions. Of the sixty-four different symbols which can be formed in this fashion, twenty-six represent letters. Other symbols in both codes are assigned to numbers, and in the Braille code to a variety of punctuation and other auxiliary marks.

How many elements of this sort should we expect to find in the characters of the written alphabet when we conceive them as code forms, and how many positions are occupied by these elements in a given alphabetic character? This question of course does not have the same import here as with the two "artificial" codes mentioned above. Asked in connection with the alphabet for our purposes, it is more a question of procedure than a question of fact. Since the Roman alphabet has not been deliberately constructed to accommodate a particular group of languages, there is no reason to seek for one and only one "right" way of breaking its characters down into a small number of elements. Yet for practical reasons we would hope to be able to treat the written alphabet as a code without generating elements or combinations much more numerous than those in the Braille or Morse codes. For one thing, it would be difficult to prepare the machine to discriminate unambiguously among more than a few different elements without reference to shape or topological features, as required by our analysis. For another, code forms involving combinations of many elements for each character involve correspondingly many possibilities of error in the identification of these characters. Also, any code consisting of more than a few elements ordered in more than a few positions would be "uneconomical" in the sense of providing far more possible alternative combinations than are needed to represent the twenty-six letters of the alphabet.

It has been taken as a rule of simplicity that all letters shall be represented by combinations containing the same number of elements. This means merely that if a position in a given sequence is not filled by an articulated element, it will be considered to be filled with a blank which counts as an additional element in the sequence. Some straightforward observations suggest that there should be at least three positions to be filled in each sequence (so we can say there are three "humps" in the lower-case M and three "peaks" in the lower-case W, while N and U have two "humps" and two "peaks" respectively). But how many elements should be considered available for filling these positions, and how should these elements be formed? The only criteria we have for weighing possible answers to these questions is that the resulting code be moderately "economical" (in the sense mentioned above) and that it permit a reasonably sharp distinction between any two combinations of the twenty-six taken to represent the alphabet.

One way of distinguishing among the various strokes used by most penmen which seems natural at first is to count the clockwise and counterclockwise loops (as in the lower-case G) as two elements, the "upward" and "downward" humps (as in W and M respectively) as two more, and the sharp peak (as in I, J and T) as yet another. But this way of looking at lower-case inscriptions as code forms turns out to be awkward in several respects. First, if the directional loop is taken as an unanalyzed element, there is no way of distinguishing between an E and an L. And unless we want to expand the number of elements to include both a dot and a cross (which, contrary to first impressions, would seem unnecessary, since these forms occur only twice each in a sample of the written alphabet and are sometimes omitted in practice), a similar difficulty would arise in connection with the I and the T. Second, there appears to be no straightforward way of characterizing a lower-case S uniquely as a combination of loops, humps and peaks. Again, if the nature of the strokes joining the various elements did not enter into the code, there would be no way of distinguishing among the D, the F, and the Q, all of which apparently consist of two counterclockwise loops.

A clue for devising a more satisfactory set of elements appears in the reflection that more information in some sense must be contained in the more highly inflected portions of the loops and humps than in the relatively straight segments of these forms. The thought that this is so seems intuitive, and moreover has been reinforced by some simple but very convincing experiments with line-drawings by Fred Attneave. As Attneave puts it, information is "concentrated at those points on a contour at which its direction changes most rapidly (i.e., at angles or peaks of curvature)."[1] This suggests that the code elements we are seeking might be focused upon those sections of the cursive line at which occur either sharp bends or abrupt changes in direction. It is clear, moreover, that different information is conveyed by the sharp bend and by the discontinuous change in direction, else there would be no essential distinction between the lower-case U and N. We should not presume that the information conveyed by inscribed letters is contained *only* in points of maximum inflection, however, for there are important differences between the A and the O, between the B and the F, between the E and the L, etc., which could not be accounted for under this presumption.

Considerations such as these led to an attempt to conceive of letter-inscriptions as code symbols composed of the six basic elements displayed in Table 2. Each element consists of a distinctive line stroke terminated by a distinctive maneuver in which the pen is moved into position for beginning the following stroke. All strokes which enter into letter-inscriptions are conceived as being either straight or curved, and as being curved either in a clockwise or in a counterclockwise direction. All strokes are conceived further as being terminated with either a sharp but continuous bend in the direction required for beginning the next stroke (left going into the last stoke of the J and the G, right for the last stroke of the F) or by a discontinuity (as in the I, J and T). The six elements are thus the six combinations of these three possible strokes with

---

[1] These experiments and some of the rationale behind them are discussed in "Some Informational Aspects of Visual Perception," by Fred Attneave, *Psychological Review*, LXVI (1954), 183–193. The quotation is from p. 184.

A Possible Code for the Written, Lower-Case Alphabet

The elements are strokes terminated by discontinuities or continued smooth sweeps to the next stroke, numbered as follows for the code below.

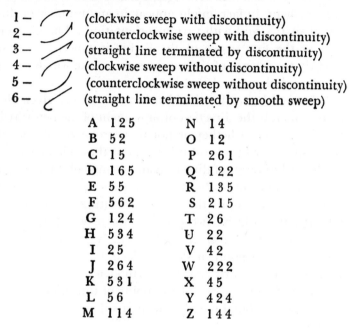

1 – (clockwise sweep with discontinuity)
2 – (counterclockwise sweep with discontinuity)
3 – (straight line terminated by discontinuity)
4 – (clockwise sweep without discontinuity)
5 – (counterclockwise sweep without discontinuity)
6 – (straight line terminated by smooth sweep)

A	1 2 5		N	1 4
B	5 2		O	1 2
C	1 5		P	2 6 1
D	1 6 5		Q	1 2 2
E	5 5		R	1 3 5
F	5 6 2		S	2 1 5
G	1 2 4		T	2 6
H	5 3 4		U	2 2
I	2 5		V	4 2
J	2 6 4		W	2 2 2
K	5 3 1		X	4 5
L	5 6		Y	4 2 4
M	1 1 4		Z	1 4 4

Table 2

their two possible terminations. The blank constitutes a seventh element. It is not the case, however, that we are left with 7³ or 343 different possible code combinations. In the code presented in Table 2, the third and sixth elements occur only in the second position of the triad, and the blank occurs only in the final position. The resulting set of 120 combinations does not seem to be a notably "uneconomical" system in which to represent the twenty-six alternatives of the Roman alphabet.

It should be noted that these elements are defined without regard to particular shape or topological features. The loop resulting from the two strokes of opposite clockwise directionality in the A, for example, may be tall or squatty, round or oblong, firm or wiggly, open or closed, and so on. Any element, in fact, might appear in any number of different shapes, and with various orientations. The orientation of the first stroke of the E, for instance, is almost directly the reverse of that of the same stroke which forms the second element of that letter.

What is relevant for the identification of any given element is merely the direction of movement of the pen which inscribes it and whether or not that stroke is terminated by a smooth or by a broken line. Thus these elements can be defined in terms of direction and change of direction of the vector tangent to the cursive line. In forming the first element, for example, the stroke-generating program will permit any clockwise sweep the vector of which does not move through more than approximately 180 degrees before reaching a point of sharp inflection. And the difference between the first and the fourth element is essentially a matter of whether or not the point of inflection following the stroke contains a discontinuous change of direction in the vector.

It might be convenient in practice to provide a means of tracing through an entire letter-inscription before the process of matching begins in an attempt to locate the two or three points of maximum inflection in the figure. In general, the end of an element-stroke will be indicated by a point of maximum inflection. The major exception to this would be with the final element of some inscriptions, where there may be a relatively smooth transition into the next triad (as with the A, C or E). The occurrence of a curved stroke upwards from the base line, either three or four strokes from the last previous occurrence of such a stroke, in general will indicate the beginning of a new triad. (Such a stroke occurs in the second position of the A, so this would not count as the beginning of a new figure.)

These code elements have not yet been tested in an actual letter-recognition system. Problems undoubtedly will occur in application of the code which will require modification of the general description of the elements given here, or even modification of the code itself. The code as it stands nonetheless has two virtues: it provides an illustration of the type of code which we might expect to find embodied in the written alphabet, and it provides a specific suggestion for such a code which can be subjected to the test of practical application.

INDEX

INDEX

A

Act, 69n

Activity, 69n; see also Process

Aristotle, 86, 121

Armstrong, D. M., 157n

Attainment, 67–79, 83 ff.

Attneave, F., 299, 299n

Austin, J. L., 74n, 156n, 185

Ayer, A. J., 134n, 167n

B

Babbage, C., 27

Barnes, W. H. F., 134n

Berkeley, G., 134n

Binary number system, 230n

Binder, H. A., 32n

Block, H. D., 15n

Bobik, J., viii

Borko, H., 294n

Braithwaite, R. B., viii, 166n

C

Capability, 94–95, 98–100

Cherry, C., 21n, 36n, 40n, 107n, 204n, 237n, 285n

Chess-playing mechanisms, xiv, xv

Chisholm, R. M., 85n

Classification, 32–34, 106–113, 118–121

and Recognition, xii, xiii, xx, 42, 44, 46, 59, 203, 211, 216–218, 252–254, 292–295

Code paradigms, 255–258, 260–261, 264–269

Communication, 213–214, 222–224, 238

system of, 226, 229, 233, 238 ff.